Cloze Stories
for
Beginning Readers
Book Two

Laurence Swinburne
Stanley Bank

illustrated by
Miriam Glassman

Walker and Company
New York

Cover Design by: Jeannie Friedman
Edited by: Mary Kalbach Horan

First published in the United States of America in 1987 by Walker Publishing Company, Inc.
Typography by Universal Printing and Publishing Company, Inc., Chapel Hill, NC.

ISBN: 0-8027-9329-0

Printed in the United States of America

10 9 8 7 6 5 4 3 2 1

CONTENTS

INTRODUCTION

The cloze technique presents reading matter as a learning activity that is fun for students and widely endorsed by educators. In a cloze story, certain words are left blank in the text. The reader must insert the right word in each blank, taking cues from the context of the story and (in this series) also selecting from a list of choices for each blank.

The cloze technique has several notable features. It sharpens *comprehension* during the reading process. It develops *vocabulary* skills by requiring the reader's thought and action, not just rote recall. It spurs *prediction* of what logically is most likely to come next by demanding the students' continuing understanding of context. It focuses the reader's attention on *significant detail*, and it rewards precision in *word use* and *thinking*.

In recent years, cloze-type tests have had expanded use as a reliable measure of students' mastery of reading comprehension skills. Similarly, cloze materials are being used increasingly in reading instruction, since they can provide enjoyable and informative reading matter that engages the students' imagination at the same time that reading skills are being developed.

These two volumes present cloze stories of graduated difficulty for grades one, two, and three, which can be used remedially for grades four, five, and six. The readability runs from 1.4 through 3.0 in Book One, and from 2.4 through 3.9 in Book Two. The selections also increase in length from one to four pages each. The number of blanks per page and the number of choices per blank increase as well, so that with increased reading level come increased length and more intensive exercise work. Each book also includes eight pages of practice or remedial exercises.

The selections are based on youngsters' needs and interests: lighthearted fiction and fantasy; stories dealing with important aspects of the lives of children, such as friendship, school life, family relationships, and self-understanding; and factual material related to the lives and schooling of children.

In Book One, the student selects the correct response from among three choices per blank. The first thirty pages of text contain four blanks each; the next forty-eight pages contain five blanks each; the last thirty pages contain six blanks each. In Book Two, there are four choices per blank. The first thirty pages contain six blanks each; the next forty-eight, seven blanks each; the last thirty, eight blanks each.

The *Cloze Stories for Beginning Readers* is designed to help *beginning readers* develop the skills necessary to become independent, skilled readers. Skills are introduced sequentially, and the blanks in which each skill is practiced are indicated for the teacher in the upper right hand corner of each page. In Book One, the skills are *phonograms* (feature recognition), *main idea, details,* and word/sentence *structure.* In Book Two, practice in these skills is continued, and new skills are introduced: *relationships* (spatial, temporal, and logical), *inference, vocabulary* development, and broad context/overall *judgments.* These skills (to be discussed in detail below) are all practiced in context, so that *comprehension* is paramount throughout the exercises.

The aim of the books is twofold: to sharpen the skills essential to the beginning reader and to help the reader move toward the next stage of reading ability. The *beginning* reader recognizes letters (and groups of letters) as representing sounds and puts the sounds together to form words. But for the beginning reader, these words are units of sound, not units of meaning: Print is translated into sound (even though silently) and then that sound is translated into meaning. The next stage of development is *skilled* reading: Print is perceived as meaning by the skilled reader, just as sound is perceived as meaning by the listener. Comprehension is immediate. That is, oral language does not mediate between print and comprehension except when the reader needs to decode an unfamiliar word. Even a

INTRODUCTION

beginning reader experiences immediate comprehension when reading a number, like *8*, or a common abbreviation, like *Mrs.*

The process of immediate comprehension involves using a limited number of features to identify a unit of meaning such as a word, a phrase, or a sentence. We can recognize units of language by using only a few of the features that are available on the page. And the more we understand as we read, the fewer of these significant features we need. We recognize features, predict what is to come in the text, and check those predictions while reading. The *Close Stories for Beginning Readers* provide graded practice in this process. The skills are practiced for themselves and for the ultimate purpose of practicing feature recognition, prediction, and verification during the process of reading. The skills used to achieve mastery of the skilled reading process are the concern of this series. Unlike programs that focus on how a reader can demonstrate what he or she has read, the books help the student improve the process, quality, and power of reading itself.

USING THE BOOKS

The two volumes are designed to allow the students to work as independently as possible and still give the teacher an insight into each child's skills. The books offer the following features for teachers:

Flexibility: They can be used with students of varying ability; they can be used with a whole class, with small groups, or with individuals.

Self-correction: Students can learn to correct their own answers, using the keys; correction can be done individually, by pupil pairs, or in groups.

Diagnosis: The series includes procedures to help the teacher pinpoint specific reading problems (inference, vocabulary development, etc.) and assign remedial exercises.

First Steps with Students

The first time the material is presented, and the first time each skill is introduced, the teacher should take the students through at least one page, making the selections for the children and *explaining how they were made.* The context clues should be specifically pointed out. The children should write the correct responses in the blanks. Another page should be completed orally by the class, with individuals volunteering responses and the strategies used to make the selections. Additionally, the

teacher may take the students through a few of the exercises. The pages on which the stories appear include a list of skills practiced; the exercise pages are limited to one skill each. The teacher should choose exercises which give practice in the skill(s) the students will practice in the stories.

Before they begin work, the students should be familiarized with the list of rules below. The teacher usually will need to repeat the rules several times.

RULES FOR STUDENTS

1. Look at the whole page before filling in blanks. Try to get an idea of what the story is about, where it is taking place, and who the characters are.
2. Choose the correct word from the group of words in the margin with the same number as the blank. Make sure the number is the same. You can get your ideas from anywhere on the page—the same sentence as the blank, sentences before it, or sentences after it.
3. Write your answer in the blank.* Make sure it is the correct blank. Make sure the spelling is the same as in the margin. If it is not, correct it.
4. You may change your mind about an answer after you have filled in the blank. If you do, you may change your answer.
5. If you need help from the teacher while you are working, ask for it.

* This procedure supports language development in general, and specifically it makes students more conscious of their choices so that they will often notice errors they would have missed had they not written their answers into the sentences. This process of immediate self-correction helps train them in the verification step of skilled reading.

After the students work through a page, the teacher or a student may read the page aloud, explaining the correct answers. Although the teacher may need to intervene occasionally, the common-sense explanations given by students are usually perfectly clear: "He held the *flag*, not a *flat* or a *flap.*" Make sure that every student understands how the answer was selected. Students may work in small groups or pairs, always discussing their strategies.

Discussing strategies not only leads to better learning, it leads to practice in language skills. For example, the blanks based on word/sentence structure could lead to a student explaining, "You can't say *he hold* or *he holding*, so it must be *he held.*" The teacher could point up the explanation: "Why must it be *held*? What is the difference between *held* and *hold*? What if *holds* were on the list? Would *holds* change the meaning? Could you use *holding* by changing the sentence?"

INTRODUCTION

Students Working on Their Own

Once the students are working on their own and at their own pace, the teacher should help students who cannot complete a blank or who miss an answer. The teacher should first make sure the student comprehends the selection. If he or she does, the teacher will find the skill the student failed to use listed at the top of the page. If that skill is a repeated problem for the student, the teacher may work on that skill by using other stories in the book or by going to the exercises in the back of the book. There is at least one full page of exercises for each skill covered. Have the student fill in the appropriate blanks and always explain the reasons for his or her choice. If the student cannot explain, the teacher should give the explanation in simple, nontechnical terms. If the student cannot choose the correct answer, the teacher should make and explain the choice.

Teachers using the program with students in need of remediation in reading should begin each new skill with a full page of the exercises on that skill. The strategies used in selecting each of the answers should be explained in detail and practiced on blanks in the stories, one by one. The story may be read aloud for this purpose. The readability level of the story used in this manner is of no consequence. The students will master the strategies so long as they can follow the explanations.

Use of the program in the manner described above will help students become better readers. The discussion of strategies will help them become better learners, as well; it will also help students perform properly on cloze-based reading tests. Unlike some coaching in "test-taking techniques," it will not help them score better than their ability dictates; rather, it will help them develop the cognitive skills that will improve their reading and will allow them to show that improvement on all reading tests. (See Claire Ashby-Davis, "Direct Instruction in Metacognition: Two Instructional Methods Related to Cloze," *Kappa Delta Pi Record,* Spring, 1986, 86-90, which discusses a more difficult form of cloze used with older children, but which reports valuable research and techniques applicable to the primary grades.)

Skills Developed in the Program

Some of the skills on which this program focuses are similar to the reading skills commonly discussed, while others are less familiar. Even the traditional skills are used in a new frame of reference, though. They are approached as parts of a whole comprehension-based reading activity, not as separate testlike skills in isolation. The goal of this series is to help students at the early stages of reading become skilled readers as defined above.

At the top of each story and each exercise page, the skill to be practiced is identified by the following terms:

1. **Phonograms** (feature recognition in context). In this program, the student must use phonograms (and other features) to identify the correct word by inferring meaning (or possible meanings) and verifying those predictions by recognizing the necessary features (letters, groups of letters, length, and shape, for example) in a list of physically similar words. If a reader is misled into "recognizing" a word that is contextually inappropriate, comprehension is prevented; the incorrect selection simply doesn't make sense. Feature recognition in context gives the students practice in *using* this basic skill as they read and thus integrating it into the reading process. In most cases, it is not the particular feature that causes difficulty, but rather the problem of using the letter as a significant feature in context. The student needs practice in the process of using phonograms and other features to discriminate among similar forms while keeping predicted meanings in mind.

2. **Main Idea**. The skill called "main idea" that is frequently stressed in reading workbooks is actually the skill of selecting or naming the main idea of a passage (often "the best title"), after the student has read and comprehended the passage. This is a study skill which helps students on tests. But it is a skill which is exercised after the passage has been read.

   In these cloze books, the term implies 1) the ability to keep the central concept of a passage in mind, *while reading,* 2) the habit of doing so, and 3) the ability to use the main idea of a passage to make the contextual judgments essential to reading with immediate comprehension.

3. Grasping **Details**. The skilled reader does more than "take in" details. She or he remembers, manipulates, and organizes them. A child may be able to identify a detail in a multiple-choice test without the ability to employ detail as a tool for continuous reading. Can he or she identify details in one part of a story and relate them to another? Can she or he remember details while reading? Can he or she base predictions on details?

INTRODUCTION

4. Word/Sentence **Structure**. Students often study the grammar of sentences and the structure of words as a set of rules that govern the writing of correct English. In reading, grammar comprises all the structural elements of the language that permit us to comprehend the relationships among the elements of a sentence. This is central to deriving meaning from what we read. Word/sentence structure in this series involves the use of grammatical morphemes (elements of a word that signal grammatical structure—number, tense, part of speech, for example) to aid in the prediction of what is yet unknown or to check a prediction that has already been made.

Some students who handle structure well in speech do not use it well in their reading. That use is the key to the skill. Of course, if the teacher notices that a student has not mastered a particular principle—for example, the use of *who* rather than *which* in a certain context—the appropriate blank may be used to reinforce the teaching of the principle.

5. Spatial, Temporal, and Logical **Relationships**. The skilled reader is constantly processing information while reading. He or she does not merely come to a single conclusion after reading a passage, but rather is actively engaged in understanding relationships while reading. Any passage is a chain of spatial, temporal, and logical relationships that constantly grows and changes. The blanks are designed to provide practice in focusing on these relationships, keeping them in mind, and changing them as prompted by the text.

6. **Inference**. Inference is using evidence to come to conclusions. If a student is a skilled, active reader, she or he could fill in these blanks quickly and easily. If a student is in the earlier, beginning, stage, each blank is an unknown which must be thought through consciously. Most beginning readers read some material as skilled readers do; filling in these blanks provides for them a model of their own skilled reading. Readers in need of remediation read at the beginning stage all the time; filling in these blanks gives them practice in thinking while reading. This practice makes these cloze workbooks uniquely helpful.

7. **Vocabulary** Development. The ability to increase vocabulary through reading means accurately predicting the meaning of a word and, if the word itself is not known, assigning a tentative meaning to it. The retention of the relationships between the word and the assigned meaning is developing vocabulary through reading. In direct instruction, this skill is often broken down into context clues. But the skill is useful only if the student is able to apply it as he or she reads. The blanks labeled *vocabulary* are designed to provide practice in this skill. That is, the correct answer is not a word remembered or recognized because it has previously appeared in the passage. The student must use her or his prediction of the meaning of the correct answer and select the word based on that prediction.

It is not necessary that the answers be difficult or unusual words. The student practices vocabulary development skills even when selecting a familiar word. Conversely, the student practices the skill even when he or she does not recognize any of the possible answers, so long as she or he has the meaning in mind.

8. Broad **Context** and Overall Judgments. If a reader is to understand what he or she is reading, the basic setting or controlling idea must be kept in mind throughout the reading. A selection longer than one paragraph may include a chain of "main ideas" in various passages, but the broad context in which those ideas are developed, the overall direction of the selection, and the setting of the events are all central to understanding. A student who habitually loses sight of overall context may score well on multiple-choice reading examinations but yet be unskilled at learning from reading full-sized selections. This series is designed to help such students by focusing on broad context, the ideas behind the "main ideas" of short practice exercises.

The *Cloze Stories for Beginning Readers* are designed to give the student graded practice in each of the skills outlined above, to provide skills practice and remediation in the context of reading full selections, and to provide practice in the essence of reading—the immediate identification not only of letters and words, but of meaning, in all its dimensions.

Stanley Bank
Lehman College
City University of New York
1986

WHO IS WHO?

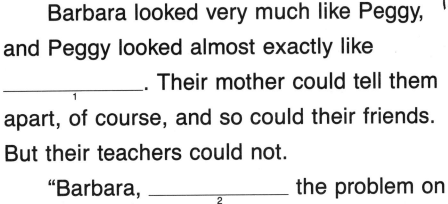

Peggy and Barbara liked being twins. They were never lonely.

Barbara looked very much like Peggy, and Peggy looked almost exactly like _____. Their mother could tell them apart, of course, and so could their friends. But their teachers could not.

1. Peggy
   Barbara
   friends
   teachers

"Barbara, _____ the problem on the board," a teacher would say. "Or is it Peggy?" It was fun _____ a while, but soon the twins wished that everyone knew who was who.

2. do
   does
   did
   doing

3. before
   for
   as
   after

One day, the eye doctor said, "You _____ need glasses. What color frames would you like?"

4. booth
   bath
   broth
   both

"Blue, because *B* is for Barbara," said Barbara.

"I want pink," said Peggy.

Teachers now tell the twins apart _____ looking at their glasses. They don't know that Peggy and Barbara wear each other's _____ sometimes, just for fun.

5. for
   of
   by
   why

6. clothes
   twins
   glasses
   eyes

The End

THE PERFECT ROOM

"Our new apartment is almost ready," their mother told Jerry and Fred. "We shall move in very soon."

"Will we have our own rooms in _____1_____ new home?" asked Fred.

"There is a room _____2_____ the two of you," their mother answered.

Jerry and _____3_____ had friends who had moved into smaller apartments. Some of them had to sleep on a folding couch in the _____4_____ room. Jerry and Fred had worried about that.

"The two of us have separate rooms now," Jerry said. "But one room is good enough," Fred said.

"What's in our _____5_____?" asked Jerry.

"Nothing, yet," said their mother. "What would you like?"

The boys started drawing. They _____6_____ for a long time, whispering to each other. At last, they showed the paper to their mother.

1. our
   we
   ours
   us

2. from
   in
   for
   as

3. Mother
   Father
   Jerry
   Fred

4. diving
   loving
   living
   liking

5. family
   weekend
   room
   couch

6. drew
   draw
   drawn
   draws

(continued)

"This is the perfect room," Jerry said. "On this wall, there is a huge TV set with a stereo next to it. The shelves are for records and video tapes."

"This is the sports wall," Fred said. "It has a place to keep our bikes and _____1_____ stuff. It has a goal for soccer practice and a target for baseballs and footballs."

"Our beds are up against this wall," Jerry said. "There are remote controls for the TV and _____2_____."

"And this wall is nothing but games," finished Fred.

Their mother looked _____3_____ the plan. "You don't have room for the door or the windows," she said. "You don't _____4_____ a dresser or a closet, either. I don't see a desk for your homework or a _____5_____ for your schoolbooks."

The boys laughed. "You can set up our room, Mom," Fred said.

"We'll _____6_____ the perfect room some other time," their mother said. "Let's save the plan."

The End

1. sports
   writing
   reading
   work

2. chess
   stereo
   television
   bike

3. through
   with
   at
   along

4. has
   had
   having
   have

5. pace
   lace
   place
   grace

6. build
   built
   builds
   building

KITTY ADOPTS SONYA

Sonya was very happy because she could have a pet. For her birthday, she could have a pet of her own.

She thought about it for weeks. Did she want a puppy, a kitten, a bird, or a _____? What should her pet be?

1. kitten
bird
fish
puppy

Sonya thought and thought. She loved puppies, but puppies did not purr, _____ kittens. She loved kittens, but kittens did not _____, like birds. She loved birds, but birds did not swim, like fish. She loved fish. But fish did not run and bark, like dogs.

2. from
because
since
like

3. sing
sings
song
sang

So Sonya kept thinking as her _____ got closer and closer.

"If you want a songbird, we must go to the pet shop," said her mother. "That shop has every kind of _____. It has cages and food for birds, too."

4. father
mother
birthday
thought

5. bird
Sonya
cat
food

"If you want a goldfish for your birthday, we must go to a different pet _____," said her father. "There is one that has every kind of fish, and it has everything for fish."

6. chop
slop
shop
stop

4   *(continued)*

Sonya knew where to get a dog or a cat. It was not a store. It was the Animal Shelter, where they save stray dogs and cats. Then people take them home, and they _____ pets.
1

Sonya decided that she did not want to buy her pet. She would go to the Animal Shelter. She would adopt her pet. "I shall go to the Animal Shelter," Sonya said. "I shall adopt my _____ there."
2

"That is a good idea," said her mother.

"Will it be a puppy or a kitten?" asked her father.

"I will _____ when I see it," Sonya said.
3

So, on her birthday, Sonya started _____ to the Animal Shelter. But she did not get very far. There, on the corner, stood a little cat. The _____ looked at Sonya. She rubbed against Sonya's legs and purred.
4
5

Sonya picked up the little cat. "You are my kitty," she said, "so your name will be Kitty. And I did not adopt you. You _____ me."
6

The End

1. become
because
either
into

2. shelter
child
doll
pet

3. now
know
knee
knot

4. walk
walks
walked
walking

5. cat
bird
girl
fish

6. bought
purred
adopted
walked

5

MOTHER'S HAND

When Allen's mother got back from the doctor's office, she was wearing a cast. It started at her elbow. It went to the ends of her fingers. She could not use her right arm or
_____ at all.
₁

The doctor said she would be fine _____ six weeks or so. But for six
₂
weeks the family would have to help her out. His sister Nancy said she would help clean. That left Allen to _____ with the
₃
cooking.

Their father left for work early in the morning. He did not come home _____ dinnertime. He would make his
₄
own breakfast every morning. Allen would help make breakfast for himself, Nancy, their _____, and their baby sister.
₅

Allen thought it would be easy because his mother would still do most of the cooking. But he _____ it would be hard as
₆
soon as his father woke him up the next morning. "It's too early, Dad," he said.

1. hard
   head
   hand
   hind

2. for
   from
   in
   to

3. eat
   hurt
   clean
   help

4. under
   until
   from
   having

5. mother
   father
   Allen
   breakfast

6. know
   knows
   knew
   known

(continued)

6

"You have to wash and dress. Then you help with breakfast," answered his father. "And make sure you are here in the afternoon to help with dinner."

"Every day?" _____ Allen.
₁

"We eat every day, don't we?" replied his father.

Allen held the bowl while his mother _____ the eggs. He had to open the
₂
milk container, but she could work the toaster _____ herself.
₃

When they finished breakfast, Allen saw his mother standing at the sink. "Wait a minute, _____," he said. "You can't
₄
wash dishes. I'll do them."

That afternoon, Allen made the hamburgers and mixed the sauce. He cut the potatoes and the carrots. He washed the salad and put it in the bowl. He cut up the _____ for the dessert. His mother
₅
showed him how to do everything.

When Allen went to bed that night, he was tired out. "Mom does more than that every day," he thought. "I shall _____
₆
her even when the six weeks have passed."

1. asked
   asking
   ask
   asks

2. mined
   miled
   mixed
   mired

3. on
   by
   at
   to

4. Dad
   Sis
   Kid
   Mom

5. front
   fruit
   fuss
   flint

6. like
   hear
   help
   wash

7

The End

THE BLOCK PARTY

Bryan lived in a nice new house on a nice street. But Bryan had no friends on the street.

It was July. Every house on Rogers Street was brand new. All the families had just moved in and were busy with their new _____ and lawns. People said hello when they saw each other, but they did not really know each other yet.

Bryan liked having friends, _____ it was not easy for him to get to know new people. "It would be different in school," he told his parents. "I can meet kids in _____. But there is no school until September." He looked out the window. "_____ how empty the street is."

His parents didn't know what to say. They didn't know their neighbors, either.

One day, Bryan's grandparents came _____ visit. His grandfather looked outside. "All these people would like _____," he said. "What you need is a block party."

(continued)

1. louses
   poses
   houses
   horses

2. so
   because
   until
   but

3. July
   town
   school
   streets

4. Look
   Book
   Took
   Hook

5. on
   at
   of
   to

6. houses
   friends
   grandparents
   school

"What's that?" asked Bryan.

"That's a big party in the street.
Everybody who lives on the block helps make
the party and everybody comes to it. By the
time the party is over, everyone has
_____ of friends."
1

Bryan's parents sent a letter to all their
new neighbors. It asked people to help make
the party. Soon, people were knocking
_____ their door and calling them by
2
phone. "I will make hamburgers," said one.

"I will _____ salad," said another.
3
"I will give out iced tea and soda," said
someone. "I will make desserts," said someone
else.

All the children on the block had jobs
_____ the party. They went to stores.
4
They helped set up tables. They helped give
out the food and drinks.

What a party it was! Everybody
_____ lots of new friends. They all
5
decided to have a block party every year.

"Next year my grandfather will come to
the _____," said Bryan. "It was his
6
idea."

The End

1. dots
   lots
   nots
   rots

2. at
   to
   over
   or

3. sell
   eat
   hate
   make

4. under
   until
   for
   after

5. make
   makes
   made
   maiden

6. school
   block
   store
   party

Skills: 1. Phonograms, 2. Structure, 3. Main Idea,
4. Relationships, 5. Details, 6. Relationships

THE BARKING FISH

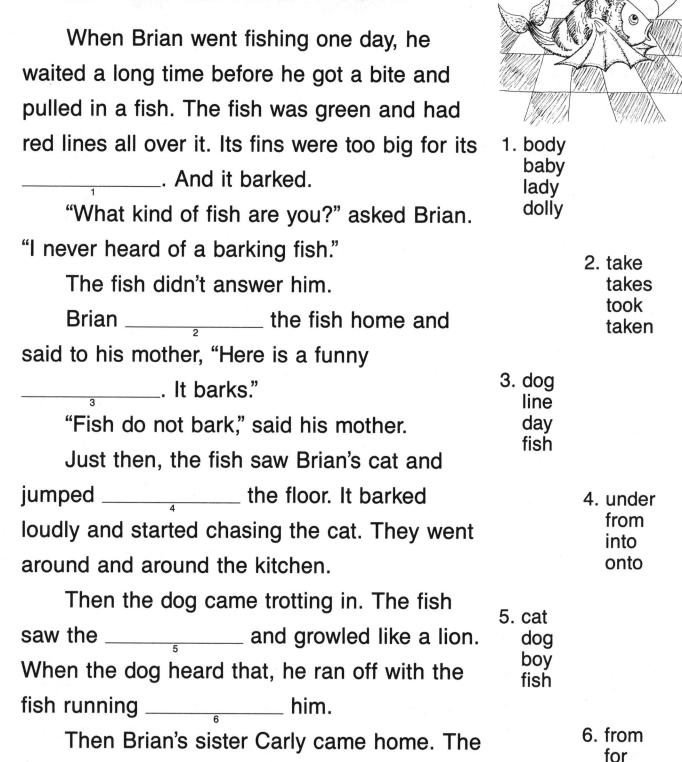

When Brian went fishing one day, he waited a long time before he got a bite and pulled in a fish. The fish was green and had red lines all over it. Its fins were too big for its

_____. And it barked.
1

"What kind of fish are you?" asked Brian. "I never heard of a barking fish."

The fish didn't answer him.

Brian _____ the fish home and
2
said to his mother, "Here is a funny

_____. It barks."
3

"Fish do not bark," said his mother.

Just then, the fish saw Brian's cat and jumped _____ the floor. It barked
4
loudly and started chasing the cat. They went around and around the kitchen.

Then the dog came trotting in. The fish saw the _____ and growled like a lion.
5
When the dog heard that, he ran off with the fish running _____ him.
6

Then Brian's sister Carly came home. The fish grunted like a bear and ran after her.

(continued)

1. body
   baby
   lady
   dolly

2. take
   takes
   took
   taken

3. dog
   line
   day
   fish

4. under
   from
   into
   onto

5. cat
   dog
   boy
   fish

6. from
   for
   after
   between

Carly ran out onto the street. There were
many children and dogs and cats out there.
The fish ran after all of them.

When Brian's father came home, his
mother said, "Brian _____ fishing and

1. gone
went
go
going

pulled in this funny fish. It barks like a dog,
growls like a _____, and grunts like a
bear. It runs after the children, the cats, and
the dogs. Brian has to take it back."

2. dog
lion
fish
cat

"Someone has to _____ it
somewhere," said Brian's father. "We don't
want it here."

3. take
fake
lake
bake

Brian's parents went out onto the street.
They threw a net around the fish and caught
it. "Take it back," they said to Brian, giving him
the _____.

4. street
fish
dog
lion

Brian took the fish back to where he had
caught it. "You are a funny fish," he said
_____ it. "I would like to keep you, but
you scare everyone but me."

5. from
for
to
on

He threw the fish back. But it was not too
late to fish a little more. He threw his line
_____ the water and pulled out a pink
and blue fish. It looked at Brian and went,
"Meow!"   *The End*

6. of
into
so
but

NEXT DOOR

The house next door was empty. Amy and
Steven hoped that a new family with children
would move in soon. Every day, they watched
_____ a moving van.
₁

A few weeks later, a big _____
₂
pulled into the driveway next door. Steven and
Amy watched from their porch.

The men carried out chairs and sofas.
They _____ a dining-room table and a
₃
big cabinet. There were pictures. There was a
big TV set. But there was no sign of the
neighbors. And there was no sign of
_____.
₄

The truck was almost empty when
another truck pulled up. Out came beds and
more _____. "Look at that," said Amy.
₅
"There are two smaller beds. They must have
children."

As soon as she said it, out came a
parade _____ children's stuff. There
₆
were games and toys and two bikes. But
where were the people?   *(continued)*

1. on
   at
   for
   through

2. trick
   track
   trunk
   truck

3. carry
   carried
   carries
   carrying

4. children
   neighbors
   trucks
   chairs

5. tables
   children
   lamps
   dishes

6. for
   through
   of
   or

At last, a car parked in front of the house. Out came the new family, who headed for their house. The two children went first. They hopped out of the car and scrambled into the house _____ their big red dog.

1. of
   for
   with
   under

Steven and _____ did not get a good look at them, but Steven said, "They look about our age. And the dog looks like fun."

2. Andy
   Amy
   Mary
   Steven

Amy took a quick look at the grown-ups walking into the _____. "Do you see what I see?" she asked.

3. house
   truck
   school
   car

Steven looked, but the adults _____ already inside. "What did you see?" he asked.

4. is
   was
   were
   are

"We know those people," Amy said. "My teacher, Mrs. Nichols. Your teacher, Mr. Nichols. Our teachers are our new neighbors."

"We may be in trouble," Steven said.

5. labor
   later
   latter
   hatter

The Nichols came over to visit _____ that day. The children became good friends. And Mrs. Nichols said, "At school, we are your _____. But at home, we are just your good neighbors."

6. neighbors
   friends
   teachers
   parents

The End

13

APRIL FOOL

Were you ever an April Fool? Were you ever tricked on the first day of April? Did you ever trick a friend and then call, "April Fool"?

Why do we like to trick people _____ April first? We do not trick them on any other day, such as January _____, which is New Year's Day. We say, "Happy New Year," but on April Fool's Day we shout, "April Fool!" Do _____ two days have anything to do with each other?

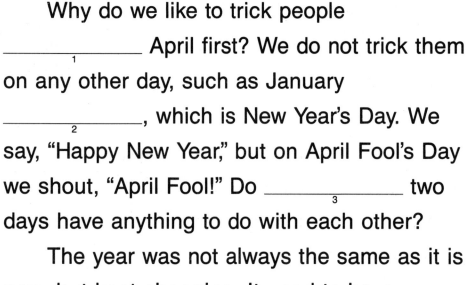

The year was not always the same as it is now, but kept changing. It used to have thirteen _____. Leap year had an extra month in it, and New Year's Day was in March. People thought the new _____ should start in the spring, so they put New Year's Day on March 21. They had parties. It was a very important holiday, so important that it took more than one day. It lasted twelve days. How would you like a holiday that is _____ days long?

(continued)

1. of
   on
   from
   into

2. frost
   fist
   first
   fines

3. them
   they
   these
   then

4. mouths
   months
   moths
   mounts

5. trick
   day
   year
   fool

6. two
   twelve
   only
   twenty

The last day was the best. People dressed up, shouted greetings, and gave presents. It was a wonderful holiday, and it was on April first.

Then things changed. New Year's Day was _____. It happened around four hundred years ago. January first became New Year's Day. Many people liked the change. But many people did not.

Would you like it if your birthday _____? Most people would not. That is why people did not like it when New Year's Day changed. A lot of them still had _____ on April first. They still dressed up, said "Happy New Year," and had a fine time.

But some other _____ thought they were silly. "Look at those fools," they said. "They do not know _____ New Year's Day is. They think it is in April."

"They are April Fools," some people said.

Ever since then, we have fooled our friends on _____ first, and they have fooled us, too.

The End

1. move
moves
mover
moved

2. charged
changed
chanced
charmed

3. fools
days
parties
years

4. months
days
years
people

5. when
who
how
why

6. January
February
March
April

15

HIS FATHER'S MOUSE

Samuel was not sure that he could believe what he had heard. Why would his father have a mouse?

Samuel's parents were getting dinner ready in the kitchen. They were speaking pretty _____. That's why Samuel was
1
sure his father had said, "The mouse fell off my desk again this afternoon. I'll have to be more careful _____ it."
2

Samuel's father is a lawyer. He isn't a pet shop owner. "Why would a lawyer keep a _____ on his desk?" Samuel asked
3
himself. He decided to ask his father.

His father said, "Well, you'll have to figure it out for yourself. I'll give you one hint, though. I need the mouse to do my _____." And he would not say
4
anything more about it. "Lawyers have to figure things out," his father would often say. "If you want to be a _____ when you
5
grow up, you have to learn to figure things out _____ yourself."
6

(continued)

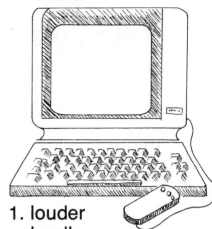

1. louder
   loudly
   softer
   softest

2. to
   with
   without
   into

3. shop
   desk
   mouse
   lawyer

4. pork
   worn
   work
   walk

5. mouse
   lawyer
   desk
   figure

6. and
   for
   on
   than

16

That's why Samuel's father often did not answer questions. He wanted Samuel to solve problems by himself.

The next day Samuel visited his father at work. He looked at the desk. There _____ books, papers, pens and pencils, and his dad's computer. There were no cages or animals, though. Samuel knew better than to ask about the _____. He was supposed to solve the problem on _____ own.

The very next day Samuel's teacher took the class to the computer room. There, Mr. Warner showed them the school's _____. The students were going to learn to use them. Each computer had a long wire coming out of it. At the end of the wire was something that looked _____ a small box.

Mr. Warner pointed to one of the small boxes and said, "That is called the mouse. You need it to control the computer. Make sure it doesn't fall off the _____ when you use it."

Samuel smiled because the problem was solved.

1. were
was
is
been

2. house
mouse
moose
rouse

3. he
her
his
him

4. classes
teachers
rooms
computers

5. over
under
like
at

6. mouse
desk
work
control

17

The End

LUNCH MONEY

Kevin had a good time on the school bus. He sat next to Adam, and they talked and laughed all the way to school.

Kevin had a long ride to school. The bus was almost empty when it picked him

_____. Then, more and more kids got

1

on as it got closer to school. Kevin had many friends, so the ride never seemed long to him.

The _____ got to school a little

2

early, so Kevin and his pals played outside for a few minutes. That was fun, too. "This will be a good day," Kevin thought.

But he figured _____. The

3

morning was fine. They had music for a while and read some exciting stories. Then the bell rang for their lunch period.

Kevin did not _____ his lunch but

4

brought money to buy it. He got in line for lunch and reached _____ his pocket.

5

But all he found was a hole in his pocket instead of his lunch _____.

6

1. first
up
next
down

2. car
taxi
bus
teacher

3. rang
rung
wrote
wrong

4. bring
brings
bringing
brought

5. into
out
from
among

6. pocket
box
money
time

(continued)

18

You would probably tell a teacher or go to the office. Many people would help you. But Kevin did not think of telling anyone. He got confused and decided to walk home.

It _____ a beautiful day. Soon he
₁
forgot about the money. He even forgot about school. He did not even notice how long he was walking.

1. been
   was
   are
   were

Once in a while, Kevin _____. He
₂
played with a dog that was also taking a walk. He looked at clothes and toys in the windows of some _____. He even played on
₃
the swings of a playground.

2. chopped
   dropped
   stopped
   strapped

3. shores
   stores
   stares
   shares

At last Kevin got to his street, at the same time the school bus did. Kevin had

_____ all afternoon! He knew he was
₄
in trouble.

4. walked
   studied
   ridden
   paid

When Kevin walked into his house, everyone rushed at him. There were his parents. _____ was his teacher. There
₅
was the principal. There was even a police officer.

5. Who
   Why
   Where
   There

They were all glad to see him. They were so _____, that he was not punished at
₆
all.

6. mad
   evil
   happy
   dizzy

The End

A HAPPY BIRTHDAY

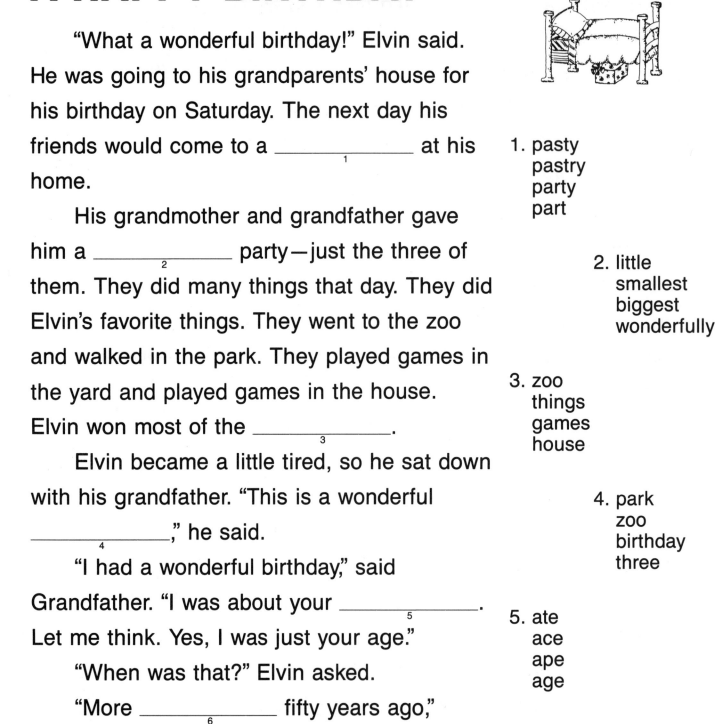

"What a wonderful birthday!" Elvin said. He was going to his grandparents' house for his birthday on Saturday. The next day his friends would come to a _____ at his home.

1. pasty
   pastry
   party
   part

His grandmother and grandfather gave him a _____ party—just the three of them. They did many things that day. They did Elvin's favorite things. They went to the zoo and walked in the park. They played games in the yard and played games in the house. Elvin won most of the _____.

2. little
   smallest
   biggest
   wonderfully

3. zoo
   things
   games
   house

Elvin became a little tired, so he sat down with his grandfather. "This is a wonderful _____," he said.

"I had a wonderful birthday," said Grandfather. "I was about your _____. Let me think. Yes, I was just your age."

"When was that?" Elvin asked.

"More _____ fifty years ago," Grandfather said. "It was just about this time of day. It was time for Uncle Ron." *(continued)*

4. park
   zoo
   birthday
   three

5. ate
   ace
   ape
   age

6. there
   their
   than
   the

20

"Uncle Ron?" asked Elvin. "Who was Uncle Ron?"

"He was not really my uncle," Grandfather told Elvin. "He had a radio program _____1_____ children. Uncle Ron sang songs and told stories. And he did birthdays."

1. for
   are
   but
   why

"How _____2_____ he do birthdays?" Elvin wanted to know.

2. do
   does
   did
   doing

"He would tell children where to look for their gifts. He would call the children by name. It was wonderful. My _____3_____ was under my bed. Uncle Ron told me to look for it there."

3. present
   grandfather
   radio
   birthday

"What was the present?" asked Elvin.

"I don't remember," said Grandfather. "But I remember Uncle Ron saying my _____4_____." He looked at his watch. "Can you tell the time?" he asked.

4. time
   game
   watch
   name

"Sure," Elvin said. "It is _____5_____ six o'clock."

5. dust
   just
   jump
   jest

Grandfather turned on the TV. A children's show began. A clown said, "Now for the birthdays. Elvin, look _____6_____ your grandparents' bed. Happy birthday, Elvin."

6. through
   over
   under
   in

The End

Skills: 1. Phonograms, 2. Structure, 3. Inference,
4. Main Idea, 5. Details, 6. Relationships

KENNY JOINS A TEAM

Kenny felt awful because his friend Brad was on the basketball team. Brad was with the team most afternoons.

Kenny's friend Jill was on the baseball team. Jill played baseball almost _____ day.

1. ever
   every
   even
   evening

Kenny's friend Ed was on the soccer _____ and played soccer a lot.

2. teamed
   teams
   team
   teaming

Kenny's friends liked him, but they were all busy with their teams. Kenny was _____ when his friends were with their teams.

3. happy
   busy
   playing
   lonely

"Why don't you join a team?" Jill asked.

"We will help you," Ed said.

"We will find your best _____," Brad said. "You don't have to be tall to play basketball. Maybe you can play _____."

4. time
   friend
   sport
   school

5. baseball
   basketball
   soccer
   football

They all went to the gym. Kenny tried to shoot baskets, but he had no luck at all. The ball never went _____ the basket.

"You are not a basketball player," his friends said.

6. over
   under
   near
   before

(continued)

22

"You don't have to be fast to play baseball," Jill said. "Maybe you can play baseball." They went to the baseball diamond, where Kenny tried to hit the ball. He was terrible. He didn't _____ it at all.
₁

"You are not a baseball player," his friends said.

"I can teach you soccer," Ed said. "Then you can _____ the team."
₂

They went to the soccer field. Kenny was even worse at soccer.

_____ the next time they saw
₃
Kenny, he was smiling.

"I am too busy to play with you," said Kenny. "I have to go to practice."

"Practice?" they said. "What _____ could you be on?"
₄

"A team we never thought of," said Kenny. "What is my best subject?"

"Math," they all said.

"And I am on the math team," said Kenny. "We play other schools. The team that solves the _____ problems is the winner."
₅

Kenny smiled. "I like _____ on a
₆
team."

The End

1. catch
base
kick
hit

2. watch
like
join
cheer

3. So
Because
Where
But

4. team
practice
bus
ball

5. some
more
most
mostly

6. been
bing
bring
being

23

Skills: 1. Phonograms, 2. Structure, 3. Inference, 4. Details, 5. Relationships, 6. Main Idea

GREGORY'S GARDEN

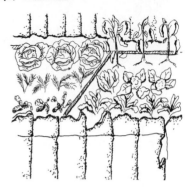

Gregory was lonely because he did not have any friends. His family had just moved to the city, and everything was strange to him.

When he lived on the _____, he was happy. He planted his own garden where he grew many vegetables. He knew how to grow things.

But there were no gardens in the city. After school, his classmates would _____ together. But Gregory did not join them because he was just too _____. He spent his afternoons all by himself.

One day, Gregory took a walk. He stopped on a street near school where there was a tall fence. A plank in the fence was loose, so he climbed through. Behind the _____ was an empty lot full of junk.

Every day, Gregory went back _____ that lot. He cleared away the junk and dug up the ground with a shovel. He was making a _____ in the middle of the big city.

(continued)

1. form
   fame
   fare
   farm

2. play
   plays
   played
   player

3. happy
   much
   shy
   young

4. walk
   fence
   school
   farm

5. on
   to
   for
   from

6. fence
   garden
   game
   street

24

It was almost the last day of school. The teacher asked, "What will you do this summer?" Some children said they were going to camp. Others were staying home. Gregory said, "I am going to work

_____ the garden."
　　　　1

The other children asked, "What garden?"

Gregory _____ them. "Can we
　　　　　　　2

see?" they asked.

After school, Gregory took some of the

_____ to see his garden. Some plants
　　　3

were already coming up. "Those are carrots,"

Gregory said. "And I have peas, and beans,

and lots of other things."

"Can I help?" asked Michael.

"Will you teach me to _____
　　　　　　　　　　　　　　　4

things?" asked Sarah.

"I can show you all how to grow things,"

Gregory said. "Everyone can _____ a
　　　　　　　　　　　　　　5

piece of this garden. But it is hard work."

The children wanted to learn anyway.

They had never had a garden before. And all

of a sudden, Gregory had lots of new

_____.
　　　6

The End

1. among
   into
   in
   of

2. told
   bold
   hold
   fold

3. vegetables
   camps
   teachers
   children

4. buy
   grow
   see
   have

5. having
   had
   have
   haves

6. fruit
   plants
   friends
   clothes

Skills: 1. Phonograms, 2. Structure, 3. Relationships, 4. Main Idea, 5. Details, 6. Inference

THE CHINESE BOWL

When Stephanie got home from school, she knew that something was different, but she could not figure out _____ it was.
She looked around the living room very carefully. Then she noticed what it was. There was a new bowl on the table in the hall.

1. hat
   chat
   whale
   what

It looked new, but it was probably an old bowl. Stephanie's mother _____ antiques. She had things that were hundreds of years old. There were dishes from England, and chairs and tables from all _____ the world. Stephanie picked up the _____, turned it over, and looked at the bottom. The writing said, "Made in China." Stephanie thought, "My mother has a new, very old Chinese bowl."

2. loving
   love
   loved
   lover

3. above
   over
   among
   forward

4. lamp
   bowl
   table
   dishes

But she didn't have it for long. As Stephanie turned it over to put it back on the _____, she felt it slip from her hands. She tried to hang on to it, but it kept slipping. She tried to grab at it before it _____ the table, but she missed. *(continued)*

5. table
   floor
   dish
   bowl

6. polished
   moved
   hit
   dropped

The bowl smashed into hundreds of little pieces.

Stephanie was not afraid of being punished. Her mother would know that she had not broken it on _____. Stephanie
1
was a careful child, as well, and her mother knew that, too.

But Stephanie knew how much her mother cared for _____ antique
2
things. She would study one for weeks before she bought it. Stephanie knew that her mother would feel terrible _____ the bowl.
3

As she picked up the _____,
4
Stephanie noticed that they seemed heavy. "That's funny," she thought, "most of Mother's _____ are delicate."
5

She saw that the colors looked very harsh and bright. "That's funny," she thought, "most of Mother's antiques are prettier than this."

Just then, Stephanie's mother came in and said, "Did you see that ugly little bowl I got at the hardware _____ for the
6
puppy's food? I think it's too ugly to keep."

The End

1. Friday
   purpose
   bricks
   time

2. its
   she
   they
   her

3. above
   under
   with
   about

4. table
   punishment
   pieces
   bowls

5. children
   antiques
   pieces
   tables

6. stone
   stove
   stole
   store

Skills: 1. Inference, 2. Details, 3. Main Idea,
4. Relationships, 5. Structure, 6. Phonograms

THE MUSEUM LOLLIPOP

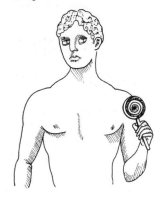

There was a candy store across the street from the museum, so Carolyn stopped there and bought the biggest, reddest lollipop. Carolyn licked it as she went into the museum. By the time she got inside, it was pretty _____.
₁

1. pink
   girl
   sticky
   red

She was in the first room, looking at a Greek statue, when a guard came over. "Sorry," he said, "you can't eat _____
₂
in the museum. You can't even carry it around. Look how sticky it is."

2. lollipops
   lunch
   statues
   guards

Carolyn didn't want to put the sticky lollipop in her pocket. She didn't want to throw it away. She didn't want to leave the _____, either. She needed someone to
₃
hold her lollipop while she looked around. But who would do it?

3. store
   museum
   guard
   pocket

She looked _____ the statue
₄
again. It was a statue of a man who looked as though he was talking to a lot of people. His arm was stretched out in front of _____, the hand half closed. It almost
₅
looked as _____ he was holding
₆
something.

4. in
   on
   from
   at

5. his
   he
   him
   he's

6. thou
   though
   thought
   through

28   (continued)

Carolyn put the lollipop into the statue's hand and walked away as fast as she could. When the guard turned around, he looked at her. She held up her empty hands and smiled _____ him.

1. at
   through
   in
   by

Carolyn looked at the paintings, the statues, and the pottery. She had lunch in the cafeteria but did not buy dessert. That was because of the _____. As soon as she thought of the lollipop, Carolyn was ready to leave.

2. rules
   lollipop
   guard
   statue

She walked back to the room. The guard _____ not there any more. But there was a man talking about the statue. "This is a _____ of the city of Athens making a speech."

3. is
   were
   was
   are

4. lesser
   ladder
   dealer
   leader

"What is he holding?" asked a woman.

He looked. "Why, that's a . . . It must be a . . . It looks just like . . . I don't know what that is."

5. guard
   statue
   painting
   door

Carolyn walked up to the _____. "Don't you know a lollipop when you see it?" she asked. She took her lollipop from the statue's hand and walked _____ out of the museum.

6. sadly
   happily
   hungrily
   limping

The End

KATE AND JIMMY

Kate stepped out of her front door. As she started to walk away, she felt something. Her shoe was sticking to the ground. She looked and saw a big blob of something sticky on her shoe. When she lifted her foot, the blob stretched. She lifted her ＿＿＿＿＿＿＿ higher,
1
and the blob stretched even more. At last, she lifted her foot high enough, and the blob stretched and snapped.

When she put her foot down, her shoe ＿＿＿＿＿＿＿ again. She had to take her
2
shoe off, hop back inside, and show her mother the sticky stuff ＿＿＿＿＿＿＿ the sole
3
of her shoe.

"It looks like chewing gum to me," said her mother.

"It ＿＿＿＿＿＿＿ be Kevin," Kate said.
4
She thought that her little brother had left the wad of ＿＿＿＿＿＿＿ in front of the door.
5

"Not me," Kevin said. "I didn't have any bubble gum today. Anyway, I never did that before, so why would I ＿＿＿＿＿＿＿ it
6
today?"

(continued)

1. step
   foot
   door
   stick

2. tapped
   laced
   stuck
   shined

3. on
   by
   between
   only

4. mist
   mast
   missed
   must

5. jelly
   sticks
   gum
   blob

6. done
   did
   does
   do

30

The next day, Kate stepped out of her front door. She didn't look down. But she should have. There it was again. She stepped into it again. She yelled, _____ yelling
₁
did no good. She had to take her shoe off again and _____ it. It was bubble
₂
gum, all right. This time the blob was even bigger.

· The next day Kate got up early and stood at a _____. She saw someone come
₃
to the door. He took a huge blob of bubble gum out of his mouth. He _____ it
₄
right in front of the door.

Kate saw who it was. It was Jimmy, a _____ boy in her class. She had
₅
never even talked to him. Why would he do this _____ her? She asked her
₆
mother.

"I don't know, dear," her mother said. "Why not ask Jimmy?"

So Kate asked him.

"I did it because I like you," _____
₇
said. "I wanted you to talk to me. And look, you are talking to me."

The End

1. so
   because
   but
   since

2. chew
   clean
   fit
   throw

3. widow
   meadow
   window
   windy

4. chewed
   left
   right
   ate

5. quiet
   quietly
   quiets
   quieted

6. of
   for
   as
   to

7. Kate
   Mother
   Jimmy
   Kevin

PARROTS AS PETS

How would you like a pet that can talk, like a parrot? Would you keep your parrot on your shoulder as some pirates did? Most people keep their parrots in _____.

1. caves
    canes
    cages
    cares

Most pet parrots are about twelve inches long. They're green, but their heads are yellow. And _____ tails may be blue, green, and red. Other kinds of parrots are _____ than three feet long, but they'd be a lot of trouble to care for. There is a very small kind of parrot, too, called a parakeet. Many _____ have them as pets.

2. its
    my
    your
    their

3. less
    more
    shorter
    lighter

When you get your parrot, it probably cannot talk. Remember, a _____ doesn't really say anything but just learns the sounds you teach it. The first step is to cover your parrot's _____ so the bird listens to you. Then say the words you want it to learn and repeat those _____ over and over. After many days, your parrot may repeat them.

(continued)

4. topple
    peppy
    quibble
    people

5. person
    parrot
    pirate
    parson

6. cage
    tail
    food
    shoulder

7. words
    parrots
    winds
    poems

It doesn't matter how long it takes to teach your parrot to talk. You'll have your pet for a long time. Some parrots live more than fifty years. You could still have your parrot when you are sixty _____(1)_____ old.

Some owners do not keep their parrots in cages. However, parrots have big strong beaks to chew wood. They can chew big _____(2)_____ in the furniture and rip cloth. Parrots can get into a heap of _____(3)_____. So it is best to keep your parrot in a cage.

Parrots come from warm countries, so they need to be kept _____(4)_____. They need fresh water and food, of course.

_____(5)_____ they are young, they like milk and bread. When they are older, they like nuts, seeds, bananas, and apples. And they love cake. So if your _____(6)_____ isn't in a cage, you have to watch your dinner plate.

Maybe you should teach your parrot to say "Thank you." Then if it steals your food it can be _____(7)_____ about it. The little thief could take a bite of cake and say "Thank you."

The End

1. year
   years
   yearly
   yearn

2. chairs
   pictures
   holes
   parrots

3. tremble
   thimble
   rubble
   trouble

4. away
   warm
   cold
   outside

5. Of
   Though
   From
   When

6. cage
   owner
   parrot
   fruits

7. quick
   polite
   eating
   angry

33

MONEY IN THE BANK

Jenny really needed ten dollars. Her parents' anniversary was next week. She had picked out the present she would give them.

_____ it was her father's birthday, her mother would give Jenny the money. Her father did the same for her mother's birthday. But this was _____ to be Jenny's first anniversary present to them.

Jenny had more money _____ than she needed, but she didn't know how to get it. Two years _____, she had opened a savings account at the bank on the corner. She had put in all the _____ she had saved. Her grandmother had put in a lot more for her. But could she get it out?

Jenny went to her desk where she kept the bankbook. She looked at the numbers in the book. To her surprise, she saw that she had two hundred dollars in the _____. She could take out the ten dollars. She would still _____ a lot left. *(continued)*

1. Who
   What
   Why
   When

2. gong
   gown
   growing
   going

3. lost
   saved
   hidden
   given

4. later
   above
   before
   behind

5. medals
   accounts
   money
   books

6. drawer
   bank
   bag
   present

7. have
   having
   has
   hasn't

Even though she did not know exactly what to do, Jenny took the bankbook to school the next day. She went to the bank on her way home. She got there just before it _____ at three o'clock. She went up to a woman who sat behind a desk and asked her what to do.

1. opened
   closed
   bought
   read

The woman looked at the bankbook and took a slip _____ paper out of her desk drawer. She showed Jenny where to write the amount she wanted to take out, where to write the number of her account, and where to _____ her name. "Just take the bankbook and the _____ to that window," she said. "The man there is called a teller. He will give you your money."

2. of
   with
   by
   for

3. sigh
   sight
   sign
   slim

4. woman
   man
   money
   slip

When she got her money, Jenny looked in the book to see how much she had left. Now there was _____ than two hundred dollars in the account. "There has been a mistake," she _____ the woman.

5. more
   small
   large
   most

6. said
   tell
   told
   telling

"No, it is correct," the woman said. "The _____ pays you to keep your money here. You have earned more than you took out."

7. book
   bank
   window
   slip

The End

35

THE BULLDOG

Even though Henry was scared, he tried to act as though nothing was wrong. Something was very wrong, though.

"My father is getting a bulldog," he told his friends. "He has _____ wanted

₁

one. I want one, too."

But Henry didn't really want a bulldog. Bulldogs were big, _____, and

₂

probably mean, too. He thought they looked very _____.

₃

Henry and his father didn't go to pet shops, but to special bulldog kennels where _____ are born and trained.

₄

Sometimes they drove for a whole day just to look _____ a puppy. But Henry's

₅

father didn't look just at the puppy. He looked at the puppy's mother and father, sisters and brothers, aunts and uncles.

Henry looked too, and the more he looked, the more _____ he got. How

₆

could he live with a monster? They weighed about fifty pounds. They had short, _____ noses and big mouths.

₇

1. lawyers
   already
   always
   alleys

2. pretty
   strong
   soft
   playful

3. mean
   meaner
   meanest
   meaning

4. kittens
   poodles
   shops
   bulldogs

5. with
   in
   of
   at

6. scared
   happy
   dogs
   hungry

7. cute
   long
   happy
   ugly

36   (continued)

Henry did not want to tell his father that he was afraid of bulldogs. So he pretended to like them.

One day, Henry heard his father say, "We'll _____ that pup."

1

Henry looked at the pup's father. He was short, heavy, wide, ugly, and mean looking. Henry looked at the pup's mother. She was shorter, heavier, _____, uglier, and

2
meaner looking. "I can't wait to see the _____," he said, trying to smile. He

3
would have to ride for hours in the car with the young monster. "Maybe I'll live through it," thought Henry. "Maybe I _____."

4

Henry's father was carrying a tiny white puppy. The puppy was crying. Henry took one look _____ the little pup and loved it.

5
He reached out and said, "Let me _____ him."

6

Henry cuddled the puppy. The puppy would not stop licking him. Henry did not want him to stop. "May I hold him all the way home?" he asked.

"Why not?" asked his father. "He's your _____, too."

7

The End

1. feed
   give
   take
   walk

2. shorter
   wider
   heavier
   uglier

3. father
   mother
   puppy
   kennel

4. weren't
   aren't
   isn't
   won't

5. from
   at
   for
   away

6. hole
   hill
   hold
   bold

7. car
   dog
   father
   lick

THE OPEN DOOR

Henry walked as quietly as he could. He was sneaking up on his own room. He slipped in and looked at his closet. The closet door was open again. "Mother!" he _____. (1) "It's open again."

Henry's mother came upstairs. "I didn't open it," she said. "Who would want _____ (2) open your closet door? Is there a secret in your closet?"

"Well, no," said Henry, "there is no _____ (3) there now. But if I had secret stuff, I would keep it in my _____. (4) I mean, I would keep it there if it would stay secret. But someone _____ (5) opening the door."

"It's a mystery to me," his mother said.

"It is a mystery," thought Henry to himself, "but it won't stay a mystery _____." (6)

The first thing Henry did was call a meeting of his family. "If you have been opening my _____ (7) door, confess it now," he said.

No one confessed. *(continued)*

1. call
   calls
   caller
   called

2. for
   to
   so
   again

3. closet
   shoe
   secret
   door

4. close
   closed
   closer
   closet

5. peek
   coops
   keen
   keeps

6. long
   yesterday
   secret
   thought

7. room
   car
   closet
   mother's

That night, Henry closed the closet as tightly as he could. He tried to stay awake all night, but of course he fell asleep. When he woke up, the closet door was _____ .

    1. open
       closed
       there
       tight

That day at school, he spoke to a guard. "Get fingerprints," the guard said.

Henry got some flour and _____ the knob of his closet door. Then he went out to play. When he got back, the closet was open. He looked at the knob. There was a _____ , but not a fingerprint. It looked more like a paw print. "I suspect Pusso," said Henry. Pusso was the family cat.

    2. dust
       dusting
       dusted
       dusty

    3. door
       dust
       secret
       print

The next morning, Henry got under his bed and stayed very _____ . Soon, Pusso came into the room. The cat stood on her hind legs and turned the knob _____ her paw. She pulled the _____ door open and went in. Henry waited a few minutes. Then he crept to the closet and looked in. There was Pusso, taking a nap on his shoes.

    4. quiet
       quit
       queer
       quilt

    5. of
       with
       by
       to

    6. room
       bed
       closet
       window

The mystery of the open _____ was solved.

    The End

    7. cat
       door
       knob
       print

Skills: 1. Inference, 2. Main Idea, 3. Details, 4. Relationships, 5. Phonograms, 6. Structure, 7. Structure

THE SECRET CLUB

"I know what we should do this summer," said Bob. "We should have a secret club."

"Only very special people could be _____ ," said Maria, "and we could have a secret meeting place and a secret password."
$_1$

"We need a name for our club," said Bob. "But only members of the _____ will be allowed to know the name. Let's call it the . . . the—" Bob stopped and then said, "I can't think of a _____ ."
$_2$ $_3$

"Let's call it the Secret No Name Club," said Maria, "_____ that sounds mysterious."
$_4$

"It sure does," answered Bob. "Now, we have to _____ of where we should meet. How about right here in my house?"
$_5$

"Fine," said Maria. "Now we _____ to think of a secret password. How about 'No Name'?"
$_6$

"Fine," said Bob. "Now, who will be _____ to join?"
$_7$

(continued)

1. people
   secret
   members
   friends

2. school
   team
   mystery
   club

3. person
   name
   password
   member

4. because
   unless
   first
   then

5. thin
   thick
   think
   drink

6. must
   have
   can
   may

7. allow
   allowing
   allows
   allowed

You are invited to the first meeting of the Secret No Name Club at Bob's house, Saturday, 3:00 sharp.

No Name

Skills: 1. Structure, 2. Phonograms, 3. Inference, 4. Relationships,
5. Details, 6. Vocabulary, 7. Main Idea

Bob and Maria thought about the kids they knew. "Andy?" asked Maria.

"Yes," said Bob, "and how about Beth?"

Soon they had plenty of members. "I can't think of anyone else," said Maria.

"We have not left anyone out," said Bob. "Now we need to _____ them all to the first meeting. Let's do it in writing. We can sign it with the club password, 'No Name.' Let's _____ writing."

All the kids came to the meeting. They thought the idea of a secret club was a lot of _____. Then Tony asked a question. "We are _____ here," he said. "Our club has all the kids we know in it. What are we keeping a secret? Who does not know the _____?"

The kids looked around. "I guess we have always been kind of a club," said Maria.

"We have not been a secret club, though," said Beth. "We have been a _____ club. All our friends are in the _____ because all our friends are special."

1. invite
   invites
   inviting
   invited

2. star
   start
   starch
   stare

3. work
   pain
   fun
   trouble

4. every
   all
   few
   not

5. kids
   meeting
   day
   secret

6. girls'
   friends'
   boys'
   nature

7. world
   summer
   club
   password

The End

41

THE CITY FAIR

Once upon a time, in the old world, there was a fair in a big city. There was food to eat, rides to ride, and shows to see. One of the shows was given by a clown _____ 1 made the sounds of animals so lifelike that the people _____ 2 and cheered with delight. They liked it most when he squeaked like a pig.

"I _____ 3 heard anything so real," said one.

"He could probably fool a pig with that squeak," said another.

"I don't think he could fool a _____ 4," said a third. "But he certainly could fool a farmer."

Now, all this time a real _____ 5 had been listening quietly to the city people talk about the pig. He couldn't keep quiet any _____ 6, though. He said, "You city people haven't ever heard a pig squeak. That clown doesn't sound like a _____ 7 to me. I know because I hear pigs squeaking every day when I feed them."

(continued)

1. who
   he
   what
   clown

2. clipped
   clapped
   clubbed
   chipped

3. always
   never
   usually
   sometimes

4. person
   farmer
   pig
   fair

5. pig
   clown
   squeak
   farmer

6. longer
   happier
   louder
   timer

7. clown
   farmer
   pig
   another

The city people didn't like the farmer's telling them that they were wrong. "You just envy what the clown can do," they said to him. "What does a silly old _____ know, anyway?" They shouted at the farmer and laughed at him.

1. clown
   pig
   farmer
   city

The farmer climbed up _____ the stage. "Come back tomorrow, and I'll teach you what a pig's squeak is _____," he promised.

2. with
   under
   from
   on

3. like
   life
   lick
   lift

The next day the farmer climbed up on the stage again. The city people gathered around and waited. They just wanted to _____ at him.

4. cheer
   squeak
   laugh
   oink

The farmer bent his head down and started making sounds that were nothing like the squeals the clown had made. The people laughed and threw rotten tomatoes at him. "Stop making that _____ noise," they shouted. "That's nothing like a pig."

5. terror
   terrible
   terribly
   terrors

The farmer straightened up and reached under his _____. "You have not been hissing at me," he said and pulled out a little pig. "This was making the _____ you say are nothing like a pig's."

6. cloak
   farm
   clown
   pig

7. hisses
   joke
   sounds
   laughs

The End

43

NAIL SOUP

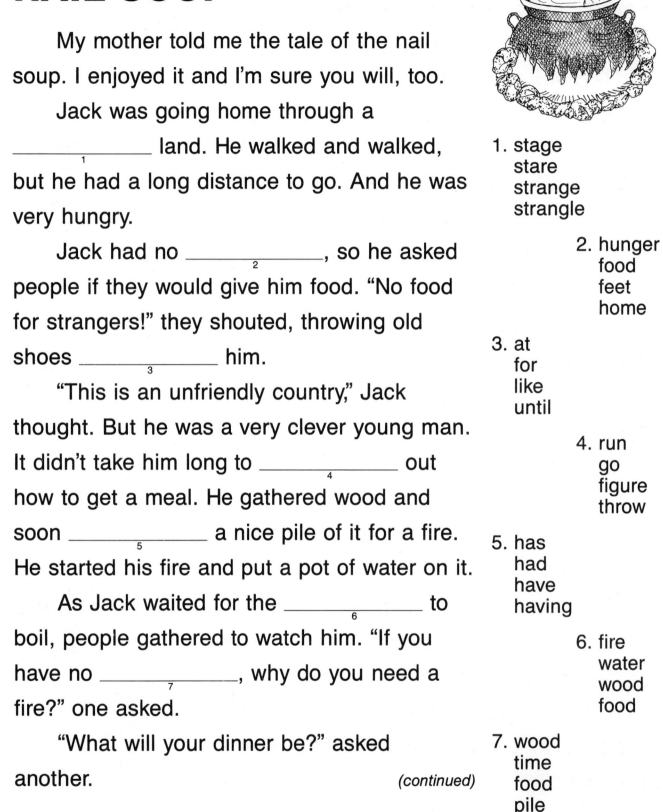

My mother told me the tale of the nail soup. I enjoyed it and I'm sure you will, too.

Jack was going home through a

_____ land. He walked and walked, ₁

but he had a long distance to go. And he was very hungry.

Jack had no _____, so he asked ₂

people if they would give him food. "No food for strangers!" they shouted, throwing old

shoes _____ him. ₃

"This is an unfriendly country," Jack thought. But he was a very clever young man.

It didn't take him long to _____ out ₄

how to get a meal. He gathered wood and

soon _____ a nice pile of it for a fire. ₅

He started his fire and put a pot of water on it.

As Jack waited for the _____ to ₆

boil, people gathered to watch him. "If you

have no _____, why do you need a ₇

fire?" one asked.

"What will your dinner be?" asked

another.

(continued)

1. stage
   stare
   strange
   strangle

2. hunger
   food
   feet
   home

3. at
   for
   like
   until

4. run
   go
   figure
   throw

5. has
   had
   have
   having

6. fire
   water
   wood
   food

7. wood
   time
   food
   pile

Jack picked up a nail from the ground. He threw it into the pot of water. "I am making nail soup," he said. "It is delicious."

"Nail soup!" said the people. "_____ every heard of nail soup? There is no such thing."

$_1$

"Wait and see," said Jack. "Now it is time to _____ the soup." He tasted it. "Wonderful," said Jack. "It just needs some

$_2$

_____."

$_3$

One of the people gave him salt. Jack tasted the soup again. "Wonderful," he said. "But a few carrots _____ make it better."

$_4$

One of the people gave him a few carrots. Jack tasted the soup _____ more. "Wonderful," he said. "But some beans would make it better."

$_5$

Someone gave him some beans. He tasted the _____. "Wonderful," he said. "All it needs is a bone with some meat on it."

$_6$

Someone gave him a _____. He tasted the soup. "Wonderful," he said. And he ate it all up!

$_7$

The End

1. Who
   Whose
   Their
   His

2. task
   tack
   taste
   tank

3. salt
   money
   pants
   pots

4. never
   would
   did
   wouldn't

5. once
   twice
   no
   never

6. beans
   carrots
   salt
   soup

7. punch
   dollar
   bone
   potato

Skills: 1. Main Idea, 2. Inference, 3. Relationships, 4. Structure,
5. Phonograms, 6. Details, 7. Vocabulary

AN AMERICAN KING

Of course, the United States has not been ruled by a king since it became a country. And there was never a king who was an American.

But there was once a _____ in
₁
America. He was an Indian chief the English called King Philip.

When the settlers came to New England, there were many Indian _____. King
₂
Philip thought that the settlers and the Indians could not live side _____ side. He
₃
knew that the ways of the forest Indians and the ways of the settlers were too
_____. He saw that the settlers would
₄
spread over the whole country.

The _____ were not the Indians'
₅
only enemies. Before Philip became a
_____, the Indian tribes fought against
₆
each other. That made them easy for the settlers to defeat. But Philip united the tribes into one great _____. He did what the
₇
settlers would one day do to make one country.

(continued)

1. state
   king
   country
   American

2. crafts
   rivers
   settlers
   tribes

3. by
   on
   in
   of

4. differ
   differs
   different
   difference

5. senators
   settlers
   settles
   nettles

6. Indian
   tribe
   chief
   union

7. chief
   place
   union
   Indian

46

Philip was not just another Indian chief. He was the chief of many tribes that acted together like one country. That is why Philip was called a king.

By 1675, the settlers _____ New England were already moving west. King Philip was afraid that the life of the _____ would be destroyed by the settlers unless he did something to save it. So King Philip's tribes went to war.

It was a terrible war for both sides. King Philip's army _____ at least thirteen towns, and many settlers lost their lives. Many more of the Indians were _____, as well. King Philip had to fight the settlers and also the Indians who _____ them. He was defeated and killed.

We should not forget the Indians who _____ for their land and their ways. Though they could not win, they would not give up. The great Indian leaders bravely stood up for their people. They were the first Americans, and an important _____ of our history.

The End

1. in
between
to
out

2. settlers
English
Indians
king

3. bought
rented
settled
destroyed

4. happy
killed
kings
tribes

5. help
helps
helped
helping

6. fought
sold
won
settled

7. pant
pair
part
paint

THE TALKING PICTURE

"You watch TV," said Victor's great-grandfather, "but I went to the talking pictures." He was sitting on the big armchair in Victor's living room.

The movies _____ to be called talking pictures, but Victor didn't know that.

_____ his great-grandfather had gone home, he thought about the talking pictures. "Why don't _____ talk?" he asked aloud.

"I talk," said a mysterious _____.

Victor looked around his living room but saw no one. "Who said that?" he asked, feeling a little _____.

"Why, I'm in plain view," said the voice. "Look at me."

Victor looked again, but there was still _____ one there. "Where are you?" he asked in a trembling voice.

"I am right next to the piano," said the voice.

There was no _____ in Victor's living room.

(continued)

1. under
   used
   us
   ups

2. After
   Along
   Above
   Unless

3. I
   mine
   me
   my

4. grandfather
   armchair
   voice
   Victor

5. scared
   happy
   picture
   sleepy

6. some
   that
   no
   any

7. piano
   picture
   window
   armchair

48

Then Victor had an idea. There were no other people in the living room. But there were things. "What are you?" he asked, more scared than before.

"I am a person, of course, and am standing _____ to the piano. I have been standing here for over a hundred years, an _____ century, and I need somebody to talk to."

Victor saw a picture of a woman. "Were you _____ to me?" Victor said to the picture.

The _____ in the picture smiled. "Yes," she said.

Just then, Victor's mother came in. "I see you are looking at the picture of my great-great-grandmother. That is the _____ picture we have."

His mother thought for a minute. Then she said, "You know, when I was little I heard about talking pictures. I didn't know they were movies. I used to think this _____ talked to me."

Victor looked at the picture. The woman seemed to _____ at him.   *The End*

1. talking
   next
   listening
   one

2. entire
   old
   about
   inside

3. running
   throwing
   standing
   talking

4. man
   omen
   woman
   workman

5. older
   aging
   oldest
   odder

6. picture
   piano
   grandfather
   Victor

7. laugh
   smile
   point
   run

SPECIAL CLASS

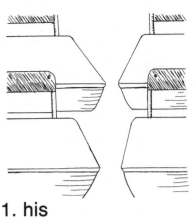

Laura was a good student. She was in every top group in her class. Laura was a good reader and writer. And she could do math better than anyone in ＿＿＿＿＿＿ class.

1. his
   those
   her
   who

Laura liked school, the work, the games, and her teacher, Ms. Jackson, very much. But what she ＿＿＿＿＿＿ best was being with her classmates.

2. liked
   hated
   taught
   wrote

She had many friends in her class, such as Nancy, who could tell very ＿＿＿＿＿＿ jokes. There was Mario, who could write plays for the class. There was Jackie, who ＿＿＿＿＿＿ not do anything special. However, Jackie was her best ＿＿＿＿＿＿ in school, and out of school, too.

3. sad
   boring
   dull
   funny

4. cold
   cool
   could
   crow

5. teacher
   friend
   joke
   play

One day when Laura came home ＿＿＿＿＿＿ the playground, her mother was smiling. "Look at this letter I got from the principal," she said.

6. from
   for
   to
   since

Laura read the letter, frowned, and said, "I don't want to go."

What did the letter say and why did ＿＿＿＿＿＿ not want to go?

7. Nancy
   Mario
   Laura
   Jackie

(continued)

50

Skills: 1. Relationships, 2. Details, 3. Phonograms, 4. Vocabulary,
5. Inference, 6. Structure, 7. Main Idea

There was going to be a special class for the best students. And Laura, who was one of the best students, had been picked for the special class.

"No!" said Laura. "But _____ 1 not?" asked her mother.

"I like my class," Laura told her. "I like my friends, too. I am not going to leave them. And Ms. Jackson is a good _____ 2. I don't want to go."

When Laura's father came home, he talked to her. But she would not _____ 3 her mind.

Then there was a knock at the door. It was Ms. Jackson. Laura's mother had _____ 4 her about the class.

"Listen, Laura," Ms. Jackson said, "I sent your name to the principal. And I sent other names, too. I sent Nancy's name, and Mario's name, and Jackie's name. None of you wants to _____ 5 your friends. But you are all _____ 6 together. And I shall be your teacher next year."

Laura smiled. _____ 7 class would be fun, after all.

The End

1. who
   where
   why
   what

2. teacher
   student
   neighbor
   class

3. charge
   charm
   change
   chain

4. paid
   called
   hired
   hated

5. leave
   like
   invite
   show

6. go
   going
   leave
   student

7. Gym
   Reading
   Special
   Kindergarten

51

A BIRTHDAY CARD

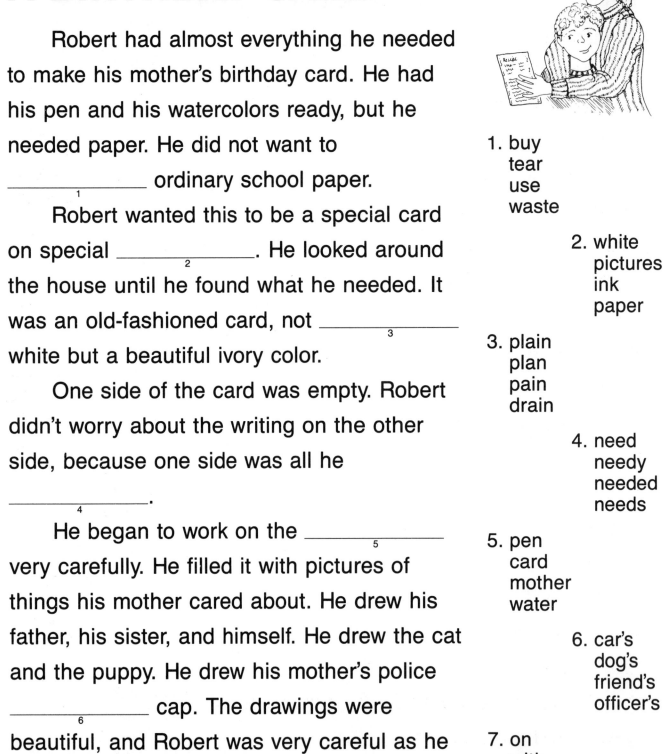

Robert had almost everything he needed to make his mother's birthday card. He had his pen and his watercolors ready, but he needed paper. He did not want to _____ ordinary school paper.

1

Robert wanted this to be a special card on special _____. He looked around

2
the house until he found what he needed. It was an old-fashioned card, not _____

3
white but a beautiful ivory color.

One side of the card was empty. Robert didn't worry about the writing on the other side, because one side was all he _____.

4

He began to work on the _____

5
very carefully. He filled it with pictures of things his mother cared about. He drew his father, his sister, and himself. He drew the cat and the puppy. He drew his mother's police _____ cap. The drawings were

6
beautiful, and Robert was very careful as he filled them in _____ watercolors.

7

(continued)

1. buy
   tear
   use
   waste

2. white
   pictures
   ink
   paper

3. plain
   plan
   pain
   drain

4. need
   needy
   needed
   needs

5. pen
   card
   mother
   water

6. car's
   dog's
   friend's
   officer's

7. on
   with
   for
   without

Skills: 1. Structure, 2. Details, 3. Inference, 4. Vocabulary, 5. Phonograms, 6. Relationships, 7. Main Idea

While he was painting, his mother and father were in the kitchen. Robert's grandmother was coming to visit that weekend, and his mother and father were getting everything ready.

"I know what _____ bake," said
                          1
his mother. "I'll make the cherry chocolate cake my grandmother used to make on holidays. She gave my _____ the
                                              2
recipe and my mother gave it to me."

"I was looking at it just yesterday," she said. "It's somewhere in the _____."
                                                                         3

"What does it look like?" asked his father.

"You'll recognize it," said his mother, "because it's in my grandmother's old-fashioned _____. I really should
              4
make a copy of it, but I never have."

Robert's father started looking _____ the kitchen. First, he looked in
    5
the drawer where the recipes and other papers were. _____ he looked in the
                              6
cabinets. Then he looked in the drawer again, but he could not find the _____.
                                                                          7

(continued)

1. ill
   I've
   I'll
   I'm

2. son
   kitchen
   mother
   grandmother

3. car
   office
   kitchen
   garden

4. desk
   handwriting
   handcar
   idea

5. ground
   around
   bound
   arrows

6. First
   Last
   Then
   Before

7. recipe
   drawer
   kitchen
   table

"If it's in the kitchen, it's hiding from me," he said.

Robert's mother laughed and said, "You were never very good at _____ things. Let me look."

₁

She looked and looked. She looked behind things and _____ things. She looked at every piece of paper in the kitchen. Her grandmother's recipe was _____.

₂

₃

"It's not just the cake," said Robert's mother. "That recipe was all I had in my grandmother's own handwriting. It is terrible to lose something like that. My birthday is _____."

₄

Just then, Robert came into the _____. "Happy birthday, Mom," he said, giving her the card. It was a beautiful card. The drawings and the colors _____ perfect.

₅

₆

"Thank you, Robert," she said. "I love this card." Then she turned the _____ over and smiled. "Now I love it even more. Here is my grandmother's recipe on the back of my birthday card."

₇

The End

1. building
   finding
   cooking
   cleaning

2. under
   behind
   before
   pretty

3. fine
   cake
   gone
   easy

4. roomed
   rammed
   ruined
   ruled

5. recipe
   cabinet
   card
   kitchen

6. looking
   become
   were
   was

7. cake
   card
   boy
   kitchen

THE INVENTOR

He was a man who went to school for only three months. That was because his teacher thought there was something wrong with him. When he grew up, he became so _____ that he could only hear shouts. 1 Yet this man was the _____ inventor 2 of all time.

Thomas Alva Edison was born in 1847 and lived in a small town in Ohio. He wondered _____ everything. He asked 3 questions all the time. "How does a hen _____ chickens from eggs? How does 4 water put out fire? What makes a balloon fly?" His mother had been a teacher, but even a teacher cannot answer every question. So young Thomas Edison learned to find answers to his _____ by himself. 5

When he was nine, Edison worked on trains. He sold newspapers and candy. After losing that _____, he sold newspapers 6 at train stations. One day, he saved a boy who was in the way of a rolling _____. 7

1. tall
   smart
   famous
   deaf

2. great
   greater
   greatest
   greatness

3. about
   under
   among
   as

4. match
   watch
   catch
   hatch

5. teachers
   inventions
   questions
   answers

6. snack
   station
   job
   railroad

7. invention
   station
   balloon
   train

(continued)

55

The boy's father taught Edison to send messages by telegraph, using the Morse Code. Soon, he was working the telegraph at a railway _____, where he invented a way of sending messages by machine

1.
_____ of tapping them out by hand. He never tried to sell that invention. His

_____ invention was a machine to
3.
count votes in the United States Congress. Congress did not buy his invention, though.

Edison realized that he should invent things people needed. A list of his inventions would fill a _____ because before he
4.
died he invented over a thousand things. Some of those things _____ human
5.
life forever.

Edison's most famous inventions are the electric light bulb and the record player. The record _____ was one of the most
6.
original inventions of all time, because no one had ever _____ of recording the
7.
human voice before. The phonograph records we play today are not very different from Edison's idea.   *(continued)*

1. track
   diner
   station
   snack

2. because
   instead
   through
   while

3. nest
   next
   neat
   extra

4. world
   list
   book
   city

5. change
   changes
   changing
   changed

6. holder
   player
   changer
   award

7. thought
   played
   sung
   complained

Other inventors had worked on a motion picture machine, but Edison's was the one that really worked. He not only gave us the electric light and the phonograph, but the movies as well. And he worked on _____(1) with sound too.

Edison did not just work on new ideas but also made _____(2) people's inventions better. After Alexander Graham Bell invented the telephone, Edison improved it so that a person would not have to _____(3) into it to be heard. He improved the typewriter, too. Before Edison worked on it, the typewriter was slower than writing by hand. After Edison's improvements, _____(4) could work much faster than that.

As you see, Edison's _____(5) were things that people needed. They included a cement mixer and a way of making rubber from a _____(6) American plant, the goldenrod. But his most famous inventions are things we use every day. Life would certainly be different _____(7) his work.

The End

1. voices
   movies
   singing
   acting

2. order
   either
   other
   armor

3. shout
   laugh
   whisper
   talk

4. writers
   talkers
   typists
   inventors

5. friends
   plants
   movies
   inventions

6. common
   commonly
   commons
   commoner

7. without
   for
   along
   therefore

A PET FOR PATRICIA

Patricia wanted a pet very much, so much that she did not care what kind of animal it was. One day, her pal Ted said, "We have two kittens, but my father says I have to get _____ of one of them. You can have it if you want."

Patricia wanted the _____ a great deal. But she said, "I'll have to ask my parents and let you know tomorrow."

"We are _____ away on a trip tomorrow," said Ted. "But I will put the kitten in the back yard. You can take it _____ you want."

Patricia went home and asked her _____ if she could have the kitten.

"You will have to take care of it," said Mother.

"I promise to take _____ of it," said Patricia.

"Then I suppose it is all right," said Father.

Something else happened that day at the zoo. A _____ forgot to lock the door of the lion's cage.

1. hair
   rid
   one
   meow

2. Ted
   yard
   kitten
   trip

3. go
   goes
   going
   gone

4. and
   if
   so
   unless

5. patents
   parties
   parents
   permits

6. cat
   have
   right
   care

7. leopard
   parent
   keeper
   lion

58   *(continued)*

The lion pushed the door open, went out of the cage, and walked out of the zoo. Then it jumped into Ted's back yard, lay down near Ted's kitten, shut its eyes, and went to sleep.

The kitten was the first to wake. When it saw the huge lion, its hair stood on end and it hissed. Then it ran away. The lion just kept on _____ .
1

Patricia was up bright and early. She dressed and ran down to Ted's back _____ for her kitten. When she saw
2
the lion, she patted it on the head and said, "Wake up, kitty."

The lion opened one eye and looked at her. It gave its meanest _____ .
3

"You have a loud meow," said Patricia. "Come along now. You are too big to _____ , so you will have to walk along
4
with me."

The lion just rolled _____ and
5
went back to sleep. But Patricia kept waking the lion up and pushing it along. Finally, the _____ went home with her. There was
6
no one at home. "I will get you some food, _____ ," Patricia said.
7

1. slopping
   sleeping
   sledding
   slurping

2. yard
   seat
   window
   street

3. meow
   yawn
   growl
   purr

4. carry
   carries
   carried
   carrying

5. through
   under
   above
   over

6. kitty
   boy
   lion
   parent

7. Ted
   Mother
   Kitty
   lion

(continued)

59

When she went into the kitchen and opened a can of cat food, the lion smelled the food and ran to the kitchen. On the way, it bumped into a table and two chairs. They fell apart _____ the lion hit them.

1. who
   when
   until
   unless

The lion _____ the cat food in one bite and looked at Patricia for more. "There is no more," she said.

2. eat
   eats
   ate
   eaten

The lion roared. Then it turned and went upstairs, because it was _____ again. It jumped on Patricia's _____. Bang! Down went the bed in little pieces. So the lion tried Mother's bed. Bang! Down it went, too. Then the lion tried Father's bed. You know what happened. Bang!

3. hungry
   angry
   sleepy
   bumpy

4. stairs
   bed
   room
   mother

At last, the lion was too tired to look for beds. It _____ went to sleep.

When Mother and Father came _____, they saw the broken table and chairs. "What happened?" they cried. "Who did that?"

5. just
   must
   rust
   gust

6. broken
   home
   roaring
   apart

"My new _____," said Patricia. "It is upstairs now, sleeping."   *(continued)*

7. bed
   lion
   kitten
   table

Skills: 1. Details, 2. Main Idea, 3. Vocabulary, 4. Phonograms,
5. Structure, 6. Inference, 7. Context

They all ran upstairs. "Look at my bed,"
said Patricia. "It is all in pieces."

"Look at my bed," said Mother. "It is all in
pieces, too."

"I don't care that my bed is in

_____," said Father. "What I care
          1
about is what is sleeping on top of the
pieces."

"Oh, that is just my kitty cat," said
Patricia.

"That is a _____," said Mother.
                    2
She picked up the telephone and called the
zoo. Five zoo men came and _____
                                              3
the lion.

"Goodbye, lion," said Patricia. "I would like
to keep you, but Mother and Father say you
are too big, eat too much, and _____
                                               4
the house apart."

Now the lion is back in the zoo, where it
is happy. Patricia is happy, too, because her
parents got her a dog. The dog _____
                                               5
on the beds. It barks a lot and leaves

_____ all over. But Mother and Father
        6
do not care, because a dog is better to have

as a _____ than a lion.   *The End*
            7

1. pieces
   blue
   rooms
   cages

2. Ted
   zoo
   lion
   pet

3. petted
   fed
   broke
   captured

4. beak
   peak
   break
   preach

5. sleep
   sleeps
   sleepy
   sleeping

6. dogs
   hair
   lions
   paws

7. kitty
   pet
   parent
   home

61

I'M NOT YOUR FRIEND

The table was all set for Meggin's birthday party. There were balloons all over and streamers hanging over the table. Everything looked just right for a _____. "You can take one plate away," Meggin remarked to her mother.

Her mother counted the place settings. "No, it looks _____ to me. We expect eleven guests, and you make an even _____. There are twelve table settings—just right."

"Just wrong," said Meggin. "Because Rebecca won't be here."

Meggin's mother thought _____ a moment and then said, "Her mother didn't call. If Rebecca were not coming, her _____ would have called."

"Her mother may not know," said Meggin, "but Rebecca _____ my friend anymore."

"Of course she is," said Meggin's mother. "She's your best _____. That's what you always say."

(continued)

1. table
   party
   friend
   balloon

2. eleven
   wrong
   setting
   correct

3. dozen
   ten
   twenty
   child

4. about
   less
   for
   far

5. mother
   thought
   party
   Meggin

6. not
   aren't
   have
   isn't

7. buy
   friend
   student
   idea

62

Skills: 1. Relationships, 2. Details, 3. Structure, 4. Vocabulary,
5. Inference, 6. Main Idea, 7. Phonograms

"That's what I always said," answered
Meggin, "but I don't say it anymore. Rebecca
told me she's not my friend, so I know she
won't come to my party."

Meggin thought _____ to what
                          1
had happened the day before. When school
let out, Meggin was waiting for Rebecca
because Rebecca's teacher always let the
class out a minute or two later than
_____ teacher did.
      2

This time, Rebecca was _____
                                    3
than usual. Meggin thought that she might be
staying after school as she sometimes did.
Rebecca liked to help her teacher put the
books back on the _____ after a silent
                         4
reading period.

Meggin noticed that Nina was waiting too,
so she _____ over to her. Nina was
            5
not really one of her friends, but Meggin was
a friendly person. "Hello," she said, "are you
_____ for someone, too?"
      6

"I don't wait for the kind of person you
do," Nina answered. "My friends are very
_____ people, not ordinary people like
      7
Rebecca."

1. of
   for
   back
   about

2. Rebecca's
   Nina's
   Teacher's
   Meggin's

3. late
   later
   latest
   lately

4. shelves
   closet
   box
   reading

5. drove
   walked
   thought
   waited

6. paying
   waiting
   working
   reading

7. special
   person
   speaking
   spanking

(continued)

Meggin thought this was a strange thing to say. But Nina was just one of those people who like to act as though they are better than anyone else. Meggin knew that it was just an act _____ Nina really didn't have any close friends. But Nina could hurt a lot of people's _____.

1.
> Then Rebecca came out of the _____ at last. When Nina saw her, she just stared at her for a moment and walked away.

> "You were talking to Nina," Rebecca said. "I'll bet she was saying _____ things about me."

> Meggin started to explain. "I was just _____ for you when . . ."

> Rebecca interrupted her. "I know the kinds of things Nina says about me. A friend of mine wouldn't listen to her. You're supposed to be my best friend, but you were standing there talking to her. I'll _____ you found plenty of nasty things to say about me, too. Well, I'm not your best friend anymore. I'm not your _____ anymore, at all."

1. because
   so
   until
   into

2. classes
   feelings
   clothing
   sayings

3. apartment
   playground
   school
   car

4. pretty
   nice
   singing
   nasty

5. wanting
   wasting
   waiting
   parting

6. hope
   bet
   agree
   doubt

7. classmate
   Nina
   nasty
   friend

(continued)

64

Rebecca walked away quickly, leaving Meggin alone in front of the school. On the walk home by herself, Meggin thought about what had happened. Nina must have _____ some nasty things about Rebecca. Rebecca's _____ must have been hurt. She must think that Meggin was saying bad things about her, too. Of course, Meggin never would do that. She was _____ to her friends.

Meggin was sad because it isn't easy to lose a friend. It's _____ harder to lose a best friend.

That's why she told her mother that Rebecca would not come to the party. Now she told her mother the whole story.

"Oh, Meggin, do children still say that?" asked her mother. "When I was _____ age, every time I had a little argument with a friend, one of us would say, 'I'm not your _____ anymore.' But we didn't mean it. I'm sure Rebecca didn't mean it, either."

When Rebecca arrived at the _____, she didn't even remember what she had said.

The End

1. thought
   said
   believed
   proved

2. fellows
   earrings
   feelings
   feeble

3. loyal
   ugly
   sad
   nasty

4. not
   best
   even
   hardly

5. you
   your
   you're
   you'd

6. argument
   daughter
   mean
   friend

7. school
   party
   feeling
   walk

UP, UP, AND AWAY

Mr. Paul came to Andy's class every week to teach lessons in science. They were mostly fun, like making glass into mirrors. Sometimes the _____ were scary, like looking at human bones.

₁

That's why Andy was happy to see Mr. Paul's car pull up to the school. He watched Mr. Paul open the trunk. Andy's seat was near the window, so he knew what was coming _____ the rest of the class. When Mr. Paul took a big tank out of the trunk of his car, Andy _____ his hand. "Mr. Paul is here," he said. "He's got a big tank or something."

Soon there was a clatter outside the _____ door. In came Mr. Paul, pulling a tank on a little wagon. He had a bag over his shoulder, too. He used the tank of gas to _____ up a balloon. It floated up to the top of the room and rested against the ceiling. "Can anyone tell us why the balloon did not fall down?" asked Mr. Paul. "Why did it fall up, _____?"

(continued)

1. glass
   lessons
   mirrors
   students

2. about
   into
   after
   before

3. washed
   raised
   bit
   saw

4. apartment
   classroom
   office
   bedroom

5. blob
   glow
   blow
   brow

6. instead
   before
   therefore
   too

No one knew, so he had to explain. "This gas is lighter than air so it makes the balloon float in the air like a boat floats in the water."

Sandy raised her hand. "Does a blimp _____ the same way?"
1

"Yes," said Mr. Paul. "Blimps and other _____ all work the same way. They
2
are big enough to carry people and go for great distances."

"Do you have a _____ in your
3
bag?" asked Henry.

"It would be fun to float _____ the
4
school," answered Mr. Paul. "But I don't have a blimp. I do have a very big _____,
5
though."

"How far would it go?" asked Andy.

"I don't know," said Mr. Paul. "How could we find out?"

"I know," Andy shouted, waving his hand in the air. "We could do an experiment."

"Right," said Mr. Paul. "You make up the _____. When you are ready, Ms. Grey
6
will call me and I'll _____ everything
7
you need."

1. worm
week
work
word

2. classrooms
people
teachers
airships

3. blimp
bag
boat
science

4. under
between
over
into

5. balloon
car
tank
sandwich

6. balloon
experiment
teacher
distance

7. bring
brings
bringing
brought

(continued)

67

The class decided to write a letter and fasten it to the big balloon. The letter would ask whoever found it to write to the class. Then, they would fill the _____ with gas and let it go.

1. room
balloon
letter
class

When Mr. Paul came, he brought a plastic bag to keep the _____ safe and dry. They decided to blow up the balloon _____, because it would be too big to go through the school doors.

2. plastic
school
letter
blimp

3. inside
outside
today
hard

They invited the principal, Mrs. Ronson. She made a long speech. While she talked, the students held on to the balloon to keep it from _____ away.

4. falling
walking
appearing
floating

Mr. Paul fastened the envelope with the letter to the balloon. "Up, up, and away!" he called. The students let go. The balloon sailed into the air. It _____ the school and then headed north. It would go wherever the winds took it.

5. circus
crinkled
crackled
circled

6. there
forever
yet
stream

"All balloons let some gas escape," said Mr. Paul, "so the balloon cannot stay up _____. The higher the balloon flies, the more gas leaks out."

A week _____.

7. pass
passed
past
passing

(continued)

68

"Maybe it's going to China," said Lisa.

"It could be on the way to the moon," said Don.

At last, a letter came. Mrs. Ronson came running into the _____ with it, right in the middle of a math lesson.
1

"Look!" she shouted. "It's in French. Our balloon has gone across the ocean to France! We'll be in the newspaper. Our balloon will be _____."
2

"Marie can read French," said Miss Grey. "She was born in Haiti."

Marie looked at the letter. "It's not from France," she said. "It's from Montreal, Canada, where many people _____ French."
3

Mrs. Ronson was _____ because
4
Montreal was not so far away. But the students were excited. They answered the letter _____ English and Marie made
5
a copy in French. Miss Grey called Mr. _____ and told him all about it. And
6
when the newspaper printed a story about the _____, Mrs. Ronson was happy, too.
7

The End

1. balloon
   ocean
   classroom
   game

2. broken
   famous
   high
   rubber

3. speak
   speaks
   speaking
   speakers

4. delighted
   disappointed
   tired
   expert

5. from
   for
   in
   into

6. Paul
   Ronson
   Marie
   Don

7. ocean
   country
   balloon
   principal

Skills: 1. Vocabulary, 2. Phonograms, 3. Inference, 4. Relationships, 5. Details, 6. Main Idea, 7. Context

THE DUNKING BOOTH

The school had a carnival every spring. The parents and teachers helped, but the students did the most. They sold tickets. They set up contests and games. Every _____ in the school had a booth.

The parents _____ in big, fancy games like a space walk. There was a merry-go-round. There was even a _____ playing marching music.

Most years, the principal just walked around and smiled a lot. _____ not this year. Oh, no, not this year. That was because of Linda and Jeffrey.

They were in Mrs. Trent's class. Mrs. _____ told them about the carnival. But she did not tell the class what kind of _____ to set up. "You must decide that," she said. "It must be fun. It must be different from all the others. And it must be the best booth in the whole _____."

"How can it be better than the space walk?" Viola asked. "How can it be better than the merry-go-round?"

(continued)

1. ticket
   class
   carnival
   year

2. broad
   bright
   bought
   brought

3. band
   game
   contest
   play

4. So
   Until
   But
   Or

5. Linda
   Jeffrey
   Booth
   Trent

6. contest
   booth
   carnival
   school

7. class
   game
   carnival
   booth

"That's right," José said. "Those are big machines. We can't make a big machine."

Mrs. Trent smiled at them. "Don't worry. People like what the students do better _____ the fancy machines. We will _____ something after lunch."

Jeffrey and Linda had lunch together. "What can we do?" asked Linda.

"Set up racing cars," Jeffrey said.

"Someone always does _____," Linda answered. "And it's boring."

"What's your idea?" Jeffrey asked.

"A wheel of fortune," Linda said.

"Someone always does that too," _____ answered. "And it's even more boring."

They thought of ring-tossing and penny-pitching. They thought of face-painting and _____-telling.

But one of them always said, "Someone always does that. And it's _____."

Linda dipped a piece of her donut into her milk. Jeffrey _____ at it and said, "That's it!"

(continued)

1. off
   since
   than
   for

2. eat
   pick
   like
   turn

3. that
   they
   there
   him

4. Linda
   José
   Jeffrey
   Trent

5. racing
   boring
   school
   fortune

6. telling
   boring
   machines
   face

7. plotted
   painted
   pointed
   poisoned

71

"What's it?" asked Linda. "Do you think we should sell milk and donuts?"

"No, no! We should have a dunking booth! People would throw balls at a target. If they _____ it, someone gets dunked."
1

"A dunking booth," said Linda. "Yes, that's it. But will Mrs. Trent let us do that? And who will get _____?"
2

"I don't care who gets dunked. I'll get dunked," Jeffrey said. He was so _____ that he bounced up and down.
3

The class thought it was a great _____. "We can call it Dunk Jeffrey,"
4
George said.

"You haven't asked me," said Mrs. Trent.

"You mean we can't have it?" asked Linda.

"That's not what I _____," she
5
said. "I mean, you haven't asked me _____ get dunked. I am willing."
6

"Oh, boy!" Jack called out. "Dunk the Teacher! Can I buy my tickets now?"

The whole _____ laughed.
7

(continued)

1. sell
   hit
   booth
   believe

2. dunce
   danced
   dunked
   ducked

3. excite
   excites
   excited
   excitement

4. class
   ticket
   carnival
   idea

5. mean
   eat
   dunk
   bounce

6. where
   to
   for
   then

7. school
   town
   booth
   class

"Now we must get permission from Mr. Garcia, the assistant principal," Mrs. Trent said. "Will the school let us have a dunking booth?"

Linda and Jeffrey went to Mr. _____ office. "A dunking booth? Dunk the teacher?" he said. "Good. But I can make it _____. I'll sit in the booth. We can call it Dunk the _____ Principal. But I had better check with Mrs. Sherman."

Mrs. Sherman was the principal. She said, "Dunk the Assistant Principal? Good. But I can make it better. I'll sit in the _____. We can call it Dunk the Principal."

_____ Jeffrey and Linda got back to their room, the class thought it was a wonderful idea. Everybody laughed and clapped. So at the _____ Mrs. Sherman sat in the booth. Students, teachers, and parents lined up to throw the ball. Most of them hit the target. Everybody laughed when Mrs. Sherman got _____. And Mrs. Sherman laughed the hardest of all.

1. Garcia
   Garcias
   Garcia's
   Garcias'

2. stupid
   better
   Tuesday
   pay

3. Old
   Chief
   Assistant
   Happy

4. both
   booth
   bath
   boots

5. From
   Since
   When
   Upon

6. carnival
   assembly
   circus
   play

7. bitten
   dunked
   left
   paid

The End

73

THE SILVER TRUMPET

Mr. and Mrs. Keeler loved music, but they only loved quiet music. When Jerry asked whether he could learn to play an instrument for the school orchestra, they said, "Of course, _____ long as it is a quiet instrument."
1.

"The violin would be nice," said Mrs. Keeler. "_____ are very important in an orchestra."
2.

"The flute would be perfect," said Mr. Keeler. "I love to _____ a flute being played softly."
3.

But the only _____ the music teacher would let Jerry have was a trumpet. "We need a _____ in our orchestra," he said. "We have plenty of violin players and more flute players than we can use. What we need are good, _____ trumpets."
4.
5.
6.

"I was afraid of this," Mrs. Keeler said. "The sound of a trumpet can be heard for blocks. We'll have to talk to the _____ about the times Jerry will practice."
7.

(continued)

1. with
   to
   as
   for

2. Violin
   Violins
   Violin's
   Violins'

3. bear
   hear
   dear
   tear

4. flute
   instrument
   orchestra
   music

5. violin
   school
   flute
   trumpet

6. soft
   loud
   string
   quiet

7. orchestra
   neighbors
   trumpets
   players

Skills: 1. Inference, 2. Structure, 3. Relationships, 4. Phonograms,
5. Vocabulary, 6. Details, 7. Main Idea

"I'm glad you're learning to play," Mr. Keeler told Jerry, "but I wish you were playing a different instrument. The trumpet just makes such a terrible _____."
1

Jerry's sister Nancy did not play a musical instrument. She took _____ lessons
2
after school, and Jerry thought she made a terrible racket _____ she practiced.
3
He never said anything, though. And when he began playing the trumpet, Nancy never complained. Jerry was grateful for that, because he knew he sounded _____.
4

Soon, Jerry was playing with the orchestra. After a while, he played all the trumpet solos, the parts of the music that the trumpet played _____. Nancy started
5
singing in school plays and at assembly programs.

One evening, _____ was
6
practicing her singing in her room while Jerry was practicing the _____ in his room.
7
Their parents were in the living room, trying to ignore the loud sounds their children were making.

(continued)

1. song
   racket
   player
   instrument

2. sing
   sings
   singing
   sang

3. who
   with
   when
   shy

4. cloud
   proud
   loud
   lord

5. alone
   together
   music
   badly

6. Jerry
   Nancy
   Viola
   Mother

7. singing
   flute
   trumpet
   orchestra

"Look at this," said Mr. Keeler, pointing to an article in the newspaper. "The governor will be making a speech in our town, and the _____ orchestra will be playing."

1. town
   state
   school
   jazz

Mrs. Keeler called to Jerry and Nancy, but of course they could not hear her. So she went _____ and brought them down. "Oh, yes," said Jerry. "We'll be playing."

2. outside
   inside
   upstairs
   downstairs

"And I will sing 'The Star-Spangled Banner,'" said Nancy. "It's very _____ to sing because it goes so high. But I am practicing very hard."

3. hard
   hardy
   hardly
   hardest

The day before the governor's _____, Nancy sang our national anthem for her parents. Just as she got to the high part, "And the rockets' red glare," she put her hand on her throat and stopped. "I hope this sore throat goes away," she said. "I can't sing the high notes _____ it does."

4. play
   music
   wedding
   speech

5. because
   until
   with
   toward

The next night, the auditorium was full. The governor was on the _____ with all the local officials. The school orchestra was _____ below the stage.

6. state
   stare
   stage
   sage

7. building
   stated
   seated
   greeting

(continued)

Then, Nancy climbed up onto the stage to sing. "Ladies and gentlemen," said the mayor, "Nancy Keeler will sing our national anthem."

The orchestra _____ the (1) introduction, and then Nancy's voice rang out. As he played, Jerry turned to watch her as she was coming to those very difficult

_____ notes. Jerry saw her hand go to (2) her throat. He knew that Nancy would not be able to go on singing.

Quick as a flash, Jerry ran up the steps to the stage. He had just gotten to the top when Nancy saw him and _____. He (3) raised the silver trumpet _____ his (4) lips and played the very high notes just in time. Then, instead of Nancy's voice, it was Jerry's _____ that finished "The (5) Star-Spangled Banner."

Everyone thought that both Nancy and Jerry were wonderful. "We're _____ of (6) both of you," said Mr. and Mrs. Keeler. "And isn't it lucky that Jerry plays such a _____ musical instrument?" (7)

1. play
   plays
   played
   playing

2. high
   low
   anthem
   trumpet

3. frowned
   coughed
   smiled
   laughed

4. of
   to
   among
   with

5. voice
   lips
   trumpet
   silver

6. prowl
   pout
   prod
   proud

7. state
   brass
   loud
   proud

The End

77

VINCENT'S VACATION

Spring vacation was on its way, and Vincent was happy about it. There would be time to play ball and to read, and those were Vincent's favorite ways to _____. Then came watching TV and sleeping late. Spring vacation was a _____ time to do all those things.

Last spring _____ had been almost perfect. His mother didn't wake him up too early, and his chores didn't take up much time. But he hadn't seen much of his father because his _____ left the house very early in the morning and sometimes worked late.

Now something else was disturbing Vincent. His mother had gone back to work only a _____ weeks before, and he was alone for an hour or so each day. Would he be alone all day during his _____? Vincent wondered if his parents had thought about that. He _____ they did, because they usually thought about everything. They did this time too. *(continued)*

1. work
   sleep
   relax
   help

2. terrible
   perfect
   cold
   school

3. weekend
   work
   vacation
   cleaning

4. mother
   father
   teacher
   vacation

5. few
   fewer
   fewest
   fairly

6. problem
   mother
   holiday
   house

7. quest
   quizzed
   guessed
   guest

Skills: 1. Inference, 2. Structure, 3. Phonograms, 4. Relationships,
5. Vocabulary, 6. Details, 7. Context, 8. Main Idea

"What am I going to do during my spring vacation?" he asked at dinner. "There won't be anyone home but me."

"You won't be home either," said his mother.

"I _____ need an assistant," said
                1
his father. "You are going to work with me this spring vacation."

That was the _____ news Vincent
                          2
had heard in a long time. His father repaired _____ machines and dryers. He went
              3
from place to place in a truck full of tools and parts _____ the machines. Vincent
              4
forgot about playing ball, reading, watching TV, and _____ late. He couldn't wait
              5
for spring vacation.

Vincent's father got him a uniform just like his own. It even said "Vincent" over the pocket. His father was named _____
                                              6
too, but his uniform said "Vince" on it.

Vincent's _____ started as his
              7
father woke him up an hour early. "Come on, Vincent, get up. We have to go to
_____."
        8

(continued)

1. don't
   really
   never
   hardly

2. good
   goodly
   better
   best

3. wishing
   waiting
   washing
   walking

4. at
   in
   for
   along

5. sleeping
   working
   eating
   coming

6. Father
   Victor
   Vincent
   Ronald

7. night
   assistant
   sleep
   vacation

8. sleep
   work
   walk
   truck

Vincent was still sleepy when they got on the train and rode to his father's business. When they got to the office, a man gave Vincent's father a list of _____. "You have a full day, Vince," he said. "You do, too, Vincent."

The father and son _____ into the truck. Vincent watched his father check the spare parts he was _____ with him. Then he gave Vincent the list of addresses. "Where to?" he asked.

Vincent read the _____ address on the list aloud. The job was a _____ dishwasher. The woman who let them in was a little surprised to see Vincent there with his _____. "You usually work alone, don't you, Vince?" she asked.

They got to work. Vincent's father found the trouble. The timer that told the dishwasher when to fill and when to drain was _____. He wrote the number of the timer on a piece of paper and gave the paper to Vincent. "Bring this part up from the _____," he said.

(continued)

1. addresses
   arrests
   admissions
   dressers

2. fell
   climbed
   skipped
   drove

3. take
   takes
   taking
   taken

4. to
   first
   for
   late

5. broken
   fine
   working
   truck

6. washer
   truck
   holiday
   father

7. white
   perfect
   running
   stuck

8. house
   truck
   train
   job

The parts were lined up by their numbers, so it was easy to find the timer. He brought it to his father right away.

As his father worked, he asked Vincent for the _____ he needed. Vincent
1
quickly learned the names of all the tools and what they looked like. He was becoming a good _____.
2

He was even better on the next job. The belt that turned a dryer around and around _____ slipped off. Vincent's father
3
tried to get it back on but could not. At last he said, "I need three _____ to do this
4
job. Vincent, you can give me that extra hand if you are _____ enough."
5

Vincent held the belt so that his father could stretch it and slip it into place. He had to _____ it with all his strength, but he
6
held on.

"I couldn't have done it _____
7
you," his father said.

Vincent's favorite way to relax is not ball-playing anymore. It is not watching TV or sleeping late, either. It is _____.
8

1. numbers
   tools
   works
   dishwashers

2. driver
   student
   truck
   helper

3. was
   are
   have
   had

4. hangs
   bands
   bangs
   hands

5. strong
   dumb
   silly
   weak

6. belt
   find
   hold
   learn

7. with
   for
   behind
   without

8. working
   thinking
   studying
   running

The End

81

THREE O'CLOCK

It is three o'clock in the morning, and of course you're in bed. Shouldn't everyone be in bed at three o'clock in the morning?

But pretend you are walking on a main _____ in your town. You pass the
1
diner that is open all night. You look in, but nobody is _____. All you see are the
2
cook and two waiters. One _____ is
3
setting the tables.

As you walk on, a police officer waves at you. He walks on, stopping _____
4
each door. He tries to open the doors, making sure they are _____.
5

A taxi goes by. The driver goes slowly because he is looking for a rider.

You see a light in the bakery. You look _____ the window and see some
6
people baking bread. You pass a television store with a television _____ in the
7
window playing a news program. You think of the people working all _____ in TV
8
and radio stations.   *(continued)*

1. bed
   idea
   street
   clock

2. eat
   eats
   eating
   eaten

3. diner
   cook
   waiter
   table

4. through
   at
   on
   under

5. open
   doors
   stores
   locked

6. throng
   through
   thrown
   trough

7. actor
   set
   radio
   show

8. ways
   parts
   stations
   night

A truck rumbles past. It stops at the corner. Two workers throw bundles of newspapers out of it. When are the newspapers printed? When are the articles written? Many news people must work at night. You see other _____. They are

1. homes
papers
clocks
trucks

full of fruits and vegetables for the stores. They are _____ from the big market. When is that market busy? When do the stores buy fruits and vegetables? When do they buy meat and _____? They do their shopping at night. Three o'clock in the morning is a busy time for them.

2. came
comes
coming
go

3. fish
paper
cars
dogs

You hear a _____ above you. It is a big airplane. You think of the pilot and the crew of an _____. Then you _____ how many people work on a ship. They cannot all be asleep, even _____ three o'clock in the morning. You can see the highway exit. There are toll booths at the exit. People are in the _____ waiting to collect money from drivers.

4. sound
sight
color
time

5. instant
airplane
hour
artist

6. wander
wonder
window
longer

7. at
on
under
for

8. cars
ships
stores
booths

You walk past the hospital where doctors and nurses are at work.

(continued)

You remember the biggest drug store in town. The sign says, "Open All Night." That means somebody must be working there right now. What if you needed _____ at three o'clock in the morning? You are glad someone is there.

1. sleep
   music
   food
   medicine

In front of the hotel, a doorman smiles at you. You _____ back. There is a clerk at the desk. Someone is sweeping the floor. You think of all the big office buildings. When do workers _____ them? They must be cleaned at night.

2. run
   talk
   smile
   throw

3. open
   close
   clean
   see

There is a big factory behind the hill. It never _____, except on Sunday. You think of all the people in that factory. You think of the people working in factories all over the _____. Many of them are working right now. They must sleep all day _____ they work all night.

4. close
   closes
   closing
   closings

5. counter
   contrary
   country
   counselor

6. although
   or
   so
   because

When some things break, people must _____ them, even at night. Water pipes must be fixed whenever they _____. What about electric lines? What about busses and taxis?   *(continued)*

7. fix
   call
   work
   make

8. light
   leak
   want
   squeak

84

You think of soldiers and sailors. Then you hear a siren. You think of fire fighters. Some of them must be working at three o'clock in the morning.

You pass a _____ on the street.
1
You know what would happen if you dialed "O." An operator would _____. There
2
are telephone people who are working at three o'clock in the morning.

The more you think about it, the more _____ you think of. You feel lucky
3
because you do not have to work at three o'clock in the morning.

You _____ past your school. Of
4
course, it is closed. You wonder what it would be like if school were _____ at night.
5
When would you have lunch? Of course, at three o'clock in the morning. You would go home at _____. That would be when
6
the day students would be coming to school. You think the _____ students are
7
lucky. You would not like being in school at three o'clock in the morning. You like being in your _____. You smile and go back to
8
sleep.

The End

1. store
policeman
telephone
dog

2. argue
call
sing
answer

3. people
times
guards
trains

4. walk
drive
ride
fly

5. upon
opera
often
open

6. twelve
dawn
midnight
eleven

7. older
night
day
reading

8. store
school
clothes
bed

85

THE INDIAN CHILD

Once there was an Indian child without a special name. He had his regular name, which was Red Cloud, but he had never done a brave or unusual deed to earn a special name. Some of his friends had _____ names, like the boy who had brought meat home when game was very _____. He was called Great Hunter. The girl who had saved her grandmother _____ the storm was called Giver of Shelter. But Red Cloud had no special _____.

In those days, American Indians hunted for their food. They also _____ berries and vegetables that grew wild. They did not farm, so when _____ was scarce, they became very hungry.

Red Cloud wanted to be a hunter. But he was not allowed to go when the hunters left the village. "Why can't I go?" he asked his _____, Flying Arrow. "I can shoot arrows from my bow as well as any _____. I can run faster and farther than most of them."

(continued)

1. special
   specially
   specialist
   specialize

2. playful
   easy
   scarce
   expensive

3. to
   from
   for
   as

4. idea
   friend
   name
   storm

5. picked
   named
   played
   let

6. weather
   clothing
   food
   time

7. lather
   father
   farther
   bather

8. hunter
   village
   berry
   game

"I will ask Old Chief," said his father.

The old Indian leader said, "I know that Red Cloud is faster and stronger than most of the hunters of our tribe. I know that Red Cloud can shoot _____ than anyone 1 else, even you. But I cannot let him go. The other hunters would be angry _____ a 2 child who can do these things better than they can."

"He wants to go so _____," said 3 Flying Arrow. "What can I tell him?"

"Send the child to me," said Old Chief.

When Red Cloud came to Old Chief, he felt very _____. After all, Old Chief 4 had been the very best of hunters. Once he had to face an angry bear without even a _____. The bear was trying to get into 5 a family's home. Old Chief had been hurt, but the _____ had turned away and run. 6 People still talked about that, and they sometimes called Old Chief by another _____, Bear Shield. 7

Old Chief said, "You cannot go with the _____." 8

1. good
   better
   best
   fine

2. at
   as
   while
   unless

3. mush
   muck
   much
   match

4. strong
   shy
   tall
   hungry

5. knife
   cub
   word
   home

6. family
   cloud
   Indian
   bear

7. day
   chief
   name
   face

8. berries
   hunters
   dancers
   children

(continued)

87

"But I want to hunt," cried Red Cloud. "I want to do something for our tribe."

Old Chief nodded. "I know how you feel," he said. "I felt that way _____ I was
1
your age. But remember, there are other ways of _____ our people than by hunting.
2
When I won the name Bear Shield, I was not with the _____."
3

For a few days, Red Cloud felt too unhappy to think about ways to _____
4
his people. But one day, while he was picking wild corn with the other children, a question came into his mind. "What makes the corn grow?" he asked _____.
5

None of his people knew. Even Old Chief said, "I _____ thought about it. It just
6
grows."

But that answer was not _____
7
for Red Cloud. He took an old corn plant and looked at it carefully. "If I put the old root in the ground, maybe a new plant will _____," he thought. But it did not.
8

(continued)

1. where
   when
   again
   that

2. help
   helps
   helping
   helped

3. tribe
   name
   hunters
   food

4. eat
   help
   kill
   annoy

5. he
   him
   himself
   his

6. never
   newer
   needer
   river

7. grown
   enough
   said
   corn

8. help
   leave
   grow
   corn

"Maybe the leaf will work," he thought. But it did not. "Perhaps it is the stalk," said Red Cloud, and he cut off part of the stalk and put it into the ground. It did not work.

"Could it be _____ of the ear?" he
                    1
asked himself. He put some kernels into the

_____. After a few days, small plants
      2
appeared. They grew and grew until they too had kernels.

Red Cloud asked his father and mother and Old Chief to see the _____, and
                                              3
he explained how he had grown them. "But what use is that?" asked Flying Arrow.

"Red Cloud has found the answer to a

_____ secret," said Old Chief. "No
      4
longer will we have to go hungry because we can't find food. We now know how to make

_____."
      5

He smiled at Red Cloud. "I am called Bear Shield. But what you have done is

greater _____ what I did. You have
            6
brought our people food for as long as time will be. You must have a special

_____, Red Cloud. You are Giver of
      7
Food, who will teach our people how to be

_____."
      8

1. pant
   park
   part
   past

2. ear
   stalk
   work
   ground

3. grounds
   Indians
   plants
   hunters

4. great
   greatest
   greatly
   greats

5. food
   clothing
   trees
   game

6. then
   behind
   into
   than

7. home
   food
   name
   time

8. hunters
   farmers
   runners
   speakers

89   *The End*

Skills: 1. Inference, 2. Phonograms, 3. Relationships, 4. Relationships, 5. Vocabulary, 6. Details, 7. Structure, 8. Main Idea

TEDDY'S LOOSE TOOTH

Teddy was getting ready for the assembly program for George Washington's birthday, and children from every grade were going to be in it. But Teddy had a _____. His

1. grade
   class
   laugh
   problem

tooth was loose.

Some kids can have a loose tooth without _____. The tooth gets loose, it falls

2. tremble
   throttle
   trouble
   thorough

out, and a new one grows in. But Teddy is _____ one of those kids. As soon as

3. like
   not
   sure
   for

one of his teeth gets loose, his tongue starts pushing and pulling _____ the tooth.

4. at
   among
   between
   or

It rocks the tooth back and forth.

Teddy would even _____ a loose

5. blow
   yell
   lick
   smile

tooth as though it were a lollipop.

Now, a front tooth was even worse than a back tooth. Teddy could use his fingers on a

6. back
   front
   new
   used

_____ tooth. He would sit in class rocking his tooth back and forth with his

7. watch
   watches
   watching
   watched

fingers until Ms. Lacey couldn't stand to _____ him any longer. "Please let that

8. Lacey
   assembly
   tongue
   tooth

tooth alone," she would say. But the next time she looked at Teddy, he would be working on his _____.

(continued)

90

His parents didn't like it, either. His father would pretend not to notice, but he noticed all right. His mother kept reminding him, "Stop it, Teddy. You _____ doing it again."

"Gee, Mom," Teddy would say, "I'm not doing it on purpose. I don't even know I'm _____ it."

"What about that assembly?" his mother would ask. "Are you going to stand in front of the _____ school pushing your tooth back and forth?"

In school, there were rehearsals _____ the assembly. Teddy would sit on the _____ with the principal, the teachers, and the other students. When the principal, Mr. Rosten, would call his name, he would get up and _____ his poem. It was the same thing every day. Mr. Rosten would say, "Very good, Teddy, but can't you stop doing that with your mouth?"

The day before the _____, Teddy decided that he had to do something. If he couldn't stop pushing, pulling, and licking that _____, he would just get rid of it.

1. been
   be
   is
   are

2. do
   does
   doing
   doings

3. whale
   whole
   whose
   wheel

4. to
   into
   under
   for

5. beach
   stage
   floor
   swing

6. write
   draw
   recite
   forget

7. assembly
   circus
   test
   vacation

8. poem
   principal
   school
   tooth

(continued)

91

TEDDY'S LOOSE TOOTH / 3

Skills: 1. Relationships, 2. Inference, 3. Structure, 4. Vocabulary,
5. Phonograms, 6. Details, 7. Phonograms, 8. Main Idea

So he made an appointment with Dr. Leonard. Of course, Dr. Leonard didn't know that Teddy had made the appointment without his parents knowing _____ it.

1. through
   around
   about
   along

When Teddy was in the dentist's _____, Dr. Leonard said, "What seems to be the trouble? Your checkup was _____."

2. home
   school
   chair
   kitchen

3. fine
   finer
   finest
   finely

"It's this tooth," Teddy said. "I have to get rid of it for the assembly."

That did not make any _____ to Dr. Leonard. "The tooth looks fine," he said. "It's almost ready to go."

4. tooth
   appointment
   trouble
   sense

"Please pull it out for me," _____ Teddy. "It has to go."

5. bagged
   begged
   bugged
   bragged

"It will go, all right," answered Dr. Leonard. "But it will _____ when it is good and ready. Nature takes care of these things pretty well." Teddy knew that it was time to _____.

6. go
   smile
   pull
   check

7. heave
   lead
   lease
   leave

At home, Teddy remembered a story about a kid who tied one end of string to his _____ and the other end to a doorknob. When someone opened the door, out came the tooth.

8. tooth
   string
   door
   kid

(continued)

92

Teddy got a string and tied it around his tooth. Then he tied the other end of the string to the knob of his bedroom door. He waited for the _____ to open. It wasn't very
1
comfortable, sitting there with the string hanging out of his _____. But nobody
2
opened the door for a long time. And the more Teddy thought about getting his tooth _____ out by the string, the less he
3
liked it. So he untied the string and threw it away.

The next morning, Teddy put on his best _____ and went into the kitchen for
4
breakfast. "Remember," said his mother. "Let that tooth alone."

Teddy nodded.

When he got to _____, Ms. Lacey
5
said, "Try to let that tooth alone."

Teddy nodded.

_____ stage, Mr. Rosten said,
6
"Teddy, let your tooth alone."

Teddy grinned. There was a big space where the loose _____ had been. "I
7
have to let it alone," he said. "It came out _____ night. It's under my pillow."
8

1. tooth
   string
   door
   mouth

2. mound
   mouse
   month
   mouth

3. cleaned
   yanked
   smoothed
   written

4. friend
   hat
   work
   clothes

5. sleep
   heaven
   school
   play

6. Over
   On
   Above
   Aside

7. dentist
   string
   door
   tooth

8. last
   lasts
   lasted
   lastly

The End

PLANET OF BALLOONS

The astronauts had a great adventure when they went to the moon. But it wasn't as great an adventure as the trip that George took not too long ago to a _____ no one even knows about.

1.
How did George get there? Well, he made a spaceship out of an _____ washing machine and some nuts and screws his father had lying around. For a space _____ and helmet, George used his father's winter underwear and an empty fishbowl.

2.

3.
George's friend Dolly made a slingshot, the biggest you ever saw. They put the spaceship in the slingshot, and George got in. Dolly pulled the _____ sling back, hollering, "Ready, set . . . go!!!" In no time _____ all, George's spaceship was _____ the moon. Turning the steering wheel, he went around the _____ to the other side. There, he saw a small object. "Funny," he said to himself. "The other _____ never said a word about that."

4.

5.

6.

7.

8.

1. plant
   plastic
   planet
   planed

2. old
   older
   oldest
   broken

3. suit
   walk
   ship
   cadet

4. huge
   tiny
   shot
   doll

5. of
   for
   at
   since

6. nearing
   burning
   cutting
   planting

7. ship
   suit
   adventure
   moon

8. slingshots
   astronauts
   children
   helmet

94 *(continued)*

George flew down toward the object. "A planet hidden from the earth," he gasped. The spaceship made a smooth _____, and George got out. He heard a laugh _____ from near his feet. He looked down and saw a strange little man who only came _____ to his knee. "Who are you?" George gasped.

"I am King Mokie," snapped the tiny man. "Why are you so big when you are talking to your king? I order you to let some air out of yourself and come down to my _____."

"I can't do that," said George.

"You mean you are not one of the balloon people?" asked the king.

"I come from a _____ on the other side of the moon," George replied.

Then the little king blew himself up as though he were a _____. Soon, he was as tall as a house and could stare down at George. "You say there is another planet on the other side of the _____? That is hard to believe." He called, "Come on out, everyone. We have a _____."

(continued)

1. sound
   sailing
   landing
   start

2. comes
   came
   goes
   coming

3. down
   along
   because
   up

4. time
   king
   sound
   height

5. ship
   planet
   sun
   balloon

6. house
   planet
   balloon
   moon

7. paper
   moon
   house
   king

8. gust
   guessed
   guest
   quest

95

Out from among the trees came many balloon people. Some were blowing themselves up, and some were losing air and getting smaller. They seemed very

_____.
      1

Suddenly a balloon girl appeared, shouting, "The needle birds are coming!"

The balloon people _____ to
              2
shake. "The needle birds are terrible," King Mokie said. "Their long beaks come to sharp points, just like _____. They dive at us
              3
and . . .," he shut his eyes and whispered, "and _____ us! Then we have to get
      4
patched. Now, we must all run to the woods and hope they won't _____ us there."
             5

"I can get rid of the needle birds," said George. "I can't be popped."

After the balloon people had hidden

_____ the trees, George took out his
      6
crayons and quickly drew a picture of a crowd of balloon _____ on a big rock. As he
           7
finished, the needle birds saw him and

_____ right at him. "Oh, oh," thought
      8
George. "This is going to hurt."   *(continued)*

1. friend
   friends
   friendly
   friendship

2. startled
   starred
   straddled
   started

3. needles
   balloons
   beaks
   points

4. kiss
   pop
   nose
   dive

5. hide
   find
   grow
   send

6. in
   into
   above
   before

7. birds
   strings
   needles
   people

8. dived
   smiled
   drew
   popped

But the needle birds saw the pictures of the balloon people on the rock. They stopped diving at George and went for the pictures instead. Bang! Bang! Bang! The needle birds hit the hard _____. Their needles fell off, all bent out of shape. The needle _____ flew away, hanging their heads.

When it was time for George to go _____, he got into his spaceship while King Mokie _____ the balloon people behind the ship. They all blew themselves up as big as they could. Then Mokie clapped his hands, and they all let out their air at once. The _____ lifted the spaceship into the sky. As he left, George looked down and waved to the balloon people. They all _____, "Thanks, and goodbye."

When he got back, George told his adventure to Dolly. "That sounds like a fine adventure," she said. "_____ time, I'm going on the spaceship and you can work the _____."

And that's what they did.

The End

1. balloons
   needles
   rock
   birds

2. brides
   bribes
   birds
   binds

3. fish
   home
   dive
   eat

4. gathered
   painted
   popped
   shipped

5. king
   air
   ship
   moon

6. shout
   shouts
   shouting
   shouted

7. First
   Last
   Next
   Your

8. balloon
   slingshot
   moon
   needle

97

Skills: 1. Inference, 2. Detail, 3. Main Idea, 4. Structure,
5. Relationship, 6. Structure, 7. Phonograms, 8. Vocabulary

THE KITE PARADE

It was a marvelous day to fly a kite, so Amy took her kite to a high spot near the pond in the park. Soon the kite was aloft. It wanted to go higher, but Amy's _____ was all used up.

Peter came up to her with his poodle, Bouncer. Bouncer got his _____ because he sort of bounced when he ran. Peter said, "Can Bouncer hold the _____?"

"He's not very big," said Amy, "but he can _____."

They attached the kite string to Bouncer's collar. Then the wind started to blow strongly, and the kite pulled harder on Bouncer's collar. Bouncer pulled _____, but the kite yanked him toward the pond. Amy and Peter sprinted after the dog. "I hope it doesn't _____ him up!" Peter shouted.

Bouncer was _____ for a small child pulling a _____ duck. Every time the wheels turned, the toy duck went, "Quack, quack!"

(continued)

1. kite
   day
   string
   parade

2. run
   name
   dog
   collar

3. spot
   park
   kite
   wind

4. try
   tries
   trying
   tried

5. below
   near
   high
   back

6. haul
   hauls
   hauled
   hauling

7. heard
   heated
   headed
   beaded

8. toy
   blowing
   pond
   air

Bouncer ran into the string the child was
pulling, and it got tangled up on one of his
hind legs.

The kite flew on, pulling Bouncer.
Bouncer bounced _____, pulling the
                    1
duck. The duck rolled along, quacking as it
rolled. Peter and Amy chased Bouncer. The
child ran after them. They were all headed
_____ the pond.
       2

At the pond, Dave's boat went, "Toot,
toot!" every few seconds. Just then, Bouncer
ran right into the water and swam along,
_____. In went the toy duck,
       3
quacking. As it went by, it caught the string to
Dave's _____. So the boat followed
              4
the duck. The duck followed the dog. The dog
followed the kite. Amy, Peter, and the child
started running around the pond, trying to
_____ up. "My boat!" Dave yelled. "My
       5
duck!" yelled the child. "Bouncer!" yelled
Peter. "My _____!" yelled Amy.
                  6

Bouncer climbed out of the other side of
the _____. The duck and the boat
            7
followed right behind him. The kids were far

_____.
       8

1. long alone above along	
	2. upon toward aside above
3. bark barks barking barked	
	4. dog boat kite duck
5. eat catch give let	
	6. boat wind life kite
7. pond bed street dog	
	8. ahead behind right over

(continued)

99

The wind blew even harder. The kite moved faster, so Bouncer and the duck and the boat moved faster, too. They were headed for Wendy, who was putting on her new roller skates _____1_____ bells on them. They missed her, but the laces of one of her _____2_____ got caught on the boat. The skate was pulled along, its bells jingling.

Wendy had one skate on, so she ran with one _____3_____ and skated with the other. She kept yelling, "My skate!" Dave was yelling, "My boat!" The child was yelling, "My duck!" Peter kept _____4_____, "Bouncer, stop! Here, boy!" Amy yelled, "My kite!" No one ever _____5_____ such yelling and barking and quacking and tooting and jangling!

Then, the _____6_____ got really strong. Every time Bouncer bounced, he was lucky to come down again. And they were all headed _____7_____ for Nancy. Her new jump rope had a whistle in the handle. Every time she turned the _____8_____, the whistle blew.

(continued)

1. when
   for
   through
   with

2. kites
   skates
   toys
   bells

3. skate
   girl
   foot
   string

4. call
   calls
   calling
   called

5. hard
   beard
   heard
   heart

6. duck
   skate
   wind
   sound

7. right
   wrong
   over
   strong

8. head
   rope
   wind
   dog

THE KITE PARADE / 4

Skills: 1. Structure, 2. Relationships, 3. Details, 4. Inference,
5. Context, 6. Phonograms, 7. Main Idea, 8. Vocabulary

When Nancy saw everybody and everything coming at her, she dropped her rope and got out of the way. The jump rope got tangled up in Wendy's skate, so it got pulled along, _____.
1

"My jump rope!" yelled Nancy. But you couldn't hear her _____ of the
2
barking, quacking, tooting, jingling, whistling, and the others yelling, "My kite!" and "Bouncer!" and "My duck!" and "My _____!" and "My skate!"
3

Now, they were headed for the hot-dog stand. Hundreds of hot dogs were piled up ready to be _____ on the grill. What
4
would happen when they ran into that?

Just then, the wind _____ down.
5
The kite started falling. Bouncer stopped bouncing. The duck, the boat, the skate, the rope, and the children _____ them all
6
stopped. The people watching cheered and clapped. "What a parade that was," they said. "It was a _____ parade."
7

The hot-dog man was so happy that he gave every one of the kids a _____
8
hot dog. And he gave Bouncer two of them.

1. to
   too
   two
   do

2. since
   into
   because
   from

3. Bouncer
   boat
   skate
   kite

4. eaten
   cooked
   iced
   played

5. stepped
   broke
   died
   aimed

6. chase
   chased
   chasing
   chases

7. police
   kite
   kitten
   winter

8. free
   bad
   written
   Bouncer

The End

THE LAMP OF TRUTH

Warren and Emily were spending the afternoon at Emily's house. It was a big, old house, so there were plenty of places to explore in it. They wandered around, looking at _____ that were never used any more. There was very little furniture in them, and it was old and strange. There were enormous _____ and small ones, so small that they almost looked like _____ chairs.

Emily knew a lot about her great-grandmother's old _____. "That's a lady chair," she said.

"If it was for a _____, why is it so small?" Warren asked, looking at the chair.

"In those days, ladies wore big hoop skirts," Emily explained. "_____ the chair were any bigger, it would have been _____ for a lady to sit on wearing a hoop skirt. If it had arms, like the other _____, a lady could not have sat on it at all."

(continued)

1. houses
   rains
   rooms
   people

2. chains
   chairs
   choirs
   shares

3. children
   childrens'
   childrens
   children's

4. business
   clothing
   ideas
   furniture

5. lady
   chair
   child
   house

6. Instead
   Although
   Since
   If

7. silly
   difficult
   wonderful
   old

8. people
   ladies
   rooms
   chairs

THE LAMP OF TRUTH / 2

Skills: 1. Inference, 2. Phonograms, 3. Relationships, 4. Context,
5. Vocabulary, 6. Details, 7. Structure, 8. Phonograms

Warren thought that Emily's house was like a museum. "Have I seen every room in the house?" he asked.

"There is still the attic," replied Emily.

The attic was like someplace in a _____(1) movie. It was full of clothing from long ago. It had boxes and _____(2), paintings, some broken chairs, and a couple of tables covered _____(3) pots and pans.

"Oh, boy," whispered Warren. "Look at all this stuff."

"You don't have to whisper," said Emily. "It's just the _____(4)."

Emily started looking at some old _____(5), holding them up to herself and looking at her reflection in a mirror. Warren found an old top hat and put it on. It was so big that it covered his _____(6). He took it off and opened a big chest that looked like a pirate's treasure chest.

The chest was _____(7) of old tools. Right on top was a brass lantern. It had a glass lens in front and a little _____(8) in back.

(continued)

1. funny
   mystery
   long
   star

2. cheese
   crests
   chests
   chess

3. from
   when
   with
   at

4. attic
   whisper
   basement
   clothing

5. cars
   dresses
   chairs
   pans

6. feet
   friend
   eyes
   attic

7. full
   fully
   fuller
   fullest

8. poor
   door
   odor
   order

"What's the door for?" he asked.

"You light the wick through the door," said Emily. "With that lens, it shines a light like a flashlight."

Warren _____ a piece of cloth
1
and wiped the lantern until he could read the writing on the lantern. "The Lamp of Truth," he

_____.
2

"There's a story about that lantern," Emily said. "If you _____ it on someone, that
3
person must tell the truth."

"Let's try it," said Warren, excited by the idea.

"We can't light matches up here," Emily said. "We need _____ to light matches
4
at all."

They went _____ and put the
5
lantern on the kitchen table. Emily went to ask her parents about lighting it.

"If you want to play _____ the
6
lantern, I have to check it," Emily's father said. "I'll put a little fuel in it, and I'll _____
7
it myself. But you must promise not to touch it and to call me if anything happens."

Soon the _____ was lit.
8

1. bound
   found
   hound
   round

2. read
   reads
   reading
   readings

3. drop
   light
   shine
   sit

4. songs
   room
   time
   permission

5. inside
   upstairs
   downstairs
   home

6. around
   with
   on
   in

7. wash
   lose
   light
   carry

8. kitchen
   lantern
   door
   attic

104   *(continued)*

Skills: 1. Relationships, 2. Vocabulary, 3. Phonograms, 4. Structure,
5. Details, 6. Main Idea, 7. Inference, 8. Context

It made a circle of light on the wall opposite the table.

"I'll go first," said Emily, and stood in the circle of light.

"Tell the truth _____ the lantern," said Warren.
1. into
   as
   while
   about

"I am afraid of it," Emily said. "I am afraid of its magic _____. I am afraid that a spirit will come out of the _____."
2. powers
   shows
   books
   ideas

She stepped out of the circle of light. "It works," she said. "I would never have said that if the lamp were not _____ on me. I would have felt silly."
3. ramp
   damp
   camp
   lamp

4. shine
   shines
   shining
   shiner

Warren got into the circle of light.

"Tell the _____ about the lantern," said Emily.
5. world
   truth
   time
   circle

"I am afraid, too," Warren said. "I am afraid that you are fooling me and this is nothing but an old _____ that gives light. I am afraid that The Lamp of Truth is just the name of the lantern. I am afraid that the _____ is over." He stepped out of the circle of _____ and they both laughed.
6. spirit
   kitchen
   lantern
   girl

7. day
   game
   lantern
   holiday

8. heat
   sound
   dirt
   light

The End

105

THE CRIME OF BOWLING

You know that bowling is a popular sport and that many people like to spend an evening in a bowling alley. You can watch bowling on television, too. Most people like to do it _____₁, though. They roll a ball along an alley and try to knock down the _____₂ pins that are on the other end.

Different kinds of _____₃ have been popular for hundreds and hundreds of years, starting thousands of years ago. People have bowled differently _____₄ the years, and even today there are different kinds of bowling. In Canada there is a _____₅ with five pins, not with ten. In the United States, people try to knock down different kinds of pins. The regular bowling pin is fifteen inches high. But the duckpin is much _____₆. The candlepin is a different shape.

Of course, many _____₇ have changed, but not many have ever been against the law. Yes, it was once against the _____₈ to bowl.

(continued)

1. them
   their
   themselves
   ourselves

2. woolen
   woody
   wooden
   warden

3. crimes
   bowling
   people
   countries

4. over
   under
   beyond
   for

5. woman
   school
   pin
   game

6. small
   smaller
   smallest
   large

7. cars
   clothes
   sports
   bowls

8. law
   rain
   pin
   wind

When the Dutch settlers came to America, they brought bowling with them. The Dutch game was called *skittles* and became very popular. If you know the story of Rip Van Winkle, you know that Rip met a group of strange-looking people _____ ninepins. Skittles used nine pins, not the ten we use today. The pins were set up in a diamond shape and the ball was rolled _____ them.

Ninepins was easy to learn and could be played indoors or on the smooth grass of a village green. Not much _____ was needed, either. If a _____ did not have the wooden clubs, or pins, they could be whittled easily. If there was no ball, round _____ could be used instead. So even in a settlement in the _____, colonists could pass the time with a game of ninepins.

By the 1900s, _____ was popular in New England, from Connecticut up north to Maine. By then, every town had its bowling alley, and no one was whittling _____ and throwing stones at them.   *(continued)*

1. play
   plays
   playing
   played

2. on
   at
   so
   from

3. playing
   Dutch
   equipment
   fun

4. torn
   town
   ton
   twin

5. stone
   stones
   stoning
   stony

6. city
   village
   forest
   colonies

7. outdoors
   green
   whittling
   ninepins

8. pins
   stones
   balls
   alleys

Pretty soon, people were betting on bowling matches. A good deal of money could be won or lost on a match. There was so much cheating by gamblers that the state of _____ decided to do something about
₁
it. But what was to be done?

It did not make much sense to forbid gambling, because the dishonest gamblers were _____ the law already. So
₂
Connecticut passed a law against bowling, because it is very hard to hide a bowling alley or to bowl without making a great deal _____ noise.
₃

That stopped the gamblers, but it also stopped the _____ bowlers. The
₄
people who loved the sport of bowling got together and read the _____ very
₅
carefully. It said that people were forbidden to bowl at nine pins. "Well," they said, "if we cannot bowl at nine _____, we shall
₆
bowl at ten pins, instead."

_____ has used ten pins ever
₇
since, even though you would not go to jail if you played _____ today.   *The End*
₈

1. England
   Holland
   Connecticut
   Bowling

2. breaking
   barking
   bricking
   booking

3. with
   among
   toward
   of

4. honest
   honesty
   honestly
   honoring

5. match
   alley
   law
   ball

6. times
   pins
   o'clock
   tens

7. Gambling
   Ninepins
   Bowling
   Jail

8. dirty
   ninepins
   house
   tenpins

1. When Jackie came near the hive, she heard the bees _____.

2. Jane read the _____ she got from the library.

3. When the refrigerator broke, the food _____.

4. The _____ is my favorite musical instrument.

5. The _____ is the largest animal alive today.

6. Billy asked his teacher what she _____ about the TV show.

7. Helen found the picture on the next _____ of the book.

8. William grew up on a _____, so he knew how to plant a garden.

9. Alice carried a _____ of water from the pool.

10. Would Ben's father _____ him to go fishing with his friends?

11. Judy wore her _____ dress to the party.

1. butting
   bussing
   buzzing
   burning

2. bike
   back
   book
   beak

3. spoiled
   sold
   spelled
   spooled

4. flat
   flute
   flit
   fleet

5. pale
   dale
   whale
   gale

6. brought
   tough
   thought
   bought

7. page
   pane
   pace
   pale

8. firm
   form
   farm
   fare

9. pole
   pal
   peel
   pail

10. allot
    alloy
    alone
    allow

11. yellow
    fellow
    alone
    allow

1. When the wind made the kite go faster and faster, it pulled very hard. When the wind died down, the _____ started to fall.

1. leaves
children
kite
cloud

2. We did many science experiments, but the best was with the balloon that sailed into Canada. We learned a lot about _____ from that experiment.

2. history
science
poems
sailing

3. The Indian boy wanted to earn a special name for a brave deed. When he helped the tribe get food, he was _____ Giver of Food.

3. fed
charged
helped
named

4. There was once a law against bowling. But people who loved the sport found a way to keep on _____ without breaking the law.

4. bowling
loving
stopping
finding

5. The first day of April is April Fool's Day, when people play tricks on each other. You had better be careful on _____ the first.

5. careful
day
grade
April

6. Carolyn could not carry her sticky lollipop around the museum. She found a place to hide it where no one expected to see a _____.

6. girl
museum
lollipop
place

1. Some people don't think of corn as a vegetable, because it is yellow, not green. They forget that potatoes and beets are not _____, either.

1. vegetables
   yellow
   green
   corn

2. When you shop, you get your food and your change. You must count your _____ to make sure it is correct.

2. shop
   change
   blessings
   fingers

3. The movers carried the chairs, a table, and lamps. The chairs and lamps fit, but the _____ was too big for the door.

3. chair
   lamp
   mover
   table

4. We did the cooking, the cleaning, the shopping, and the washing. My father and my sister did the cooking, cleaning, and washing. That left the _____ to me.

4. shopping
   cooking
   cleaning
   washing

5. When Teddy's front tooth was loose, he made a fuss. Everybody was happy when that _____ tooth came out.

5. back
   side
   front
   left

6. Soldiers, sailors, and doctors must work at night. But many people who are fire fighters, police officers, or _____ must work at night, too.

6. soldiers
   sailors
   nurses
   doctors

1. You must do your work, or you won't learn _____ much.

2. When Lon Lac came to America, he _____ learned English.

   2. quickly
   quicker
   fast
   right

3. Our police officers and fire fighters help keep us _____.

   3. save
   safe
   safety
   saver

4. Vicky won the race because she was _____ than the others.

   4. fast
   faster
   fastest
   fasting

5. There _____ too many math problems for Jonathan to finish.

   5. is
   are
   was
   were

6. Wendy is _____ to watch TV after she does her homework.

   6. allow
   allowance
   allowed
   allows

7. Andy first did his work and _____ played ball.

   7. late
   than
   then
   while

8. Mike or Alice _____ in the class.

   8. belongs
   belong
   belonging
   belongings

9. The house that Sarah and Dom live in _____ very old.

   9. were
   is
   are
   be

10. William was an _____ reader for his age.

    10. excellent
    good
    fair
    poor

11. She thought that no one was as _____ as her father.

    11. strong
    stronger
    strongly
    strongest

1. The driver _____ the car was tired.

2. Ken was so tall that he could look _____ the fence.

3. You should study _____ a test to get a perfect mark.

4. June saved her money _____ a Mother's Day present.

5. The crossing guard protects us _____ danger.

6. I hope I don't sit _____ a tall person at the circus.

7. Robert won the award _____ he was the best reader in his school.

8. Jeff wanted to be a member _____ the club.

9. The cat went by with a big dog running _____ her.

10. She sat _____ her parents on the sofa.

11. The hungry child bit _____ the apple.

1. Roger was not _____ enough to lift the heavy weight.

    1. short
    funny
    strong
    thin

2. You should not play with matches because they could start a _____.

    2. race
    fire
    fight
    match

3. Jessica's friends brought _____ to her birthday party.

    3. rabbits
    onions
    work
    presents

4. There were flowers and vegetables growing in the _____.

    4. garden
    desert
    pool
    banana

5. Jack made the soup by _____ water with food in it.

    5. drinking
    burning
    boiling
    pouring

6. The boy learned to _____ with the old pen.

    6. throw
    write
    pig
    fight

7. Jenny kept her _____ in the savings bank.

    7. clothing
    parents
    kitten
    money

8. The mystery was _____ when Henry found out who opened the door.

    8. saved
    solved
    awful
    loud

9. Sonya wanted a _____, but she could not decide between a dog and a cat.

    9. dog
    cat
    fish
    pet

10. Workers who build tunnels work far _____ the ground.

    10. below
    above
    around
    behind

11. When Victor heard the strange voice but could not see anybody, he was _____ and surprised.

    11. bored
    scared
    strange
    anybody

1. When a tooth must be taken out, the dentist extracts it. To *extract* something is to _____ it.

    1. fix
    remove
    use
    polish

2. The children watched the balloon ascend, going higher and higher. To *ascend* is to _____.

    2. fall
    ask
    rise
    watch

3. Lions, tigers, and your kitten are felines. Wild and tame _____ are all *felines*.

    3. people
    fellows
    pets
    cats

4. Matthew looked at his image in the photo. Your *image* is something that _____ like you.

    4. looks
    eats
    acts
    must

5. Vegetables are edible plants. If something is *edible*, people can _____ it.

    5. plant
    eat
    chase
    teach

6. King Philip unified many Indian tribes into one. To *unify* people or things is to bring them _____.

    6. together
    presents
    one
    home

7. On April Fool's Day, people deceive each other in funny ways. To *deceive* people is to _____ them.

    7. believe
    pay
    trick
    like

8. The clown simulated a pig's squeal so well that he sounded just like a pig. To *simulate* something is to _____ it.

    8. enjoy
    sound
    love
    copy

1. You look at the stores and houses on both sides of the street. You are walking through a _____.

   1. farm
      school
      town
      park

2. The other students watched as Jimmy did the problem on the blackboard. They were in their _____.

   2. classroom
      car
      church
      yard

3. The parrot was not in its cage but in the living room. This parrot lived in somebody's _____.

   3. zoo
      store
      tree
      home

4. You are not allowed to carry ice cream or candy through the rooms full of statues and paintings. That is a rule for being in the _____.

   4. statue
      museum
      circus
      playground

5. All of Kate's friends were gathered around the table. They clapped when Kate blew out the candles. The party was for Kate's _____.

   5. parents
      brother
      birthday
      school

6. The puppy squirmed out of Henry's arms and jumped into the front seat where Henry's father was driving. They were all in the family _____.

   6. car
      home
      yard
      dog

7. Amy's kite flew over the bushes and lawns. It was high over the fence around the playground. Amy was flying her kite in the _____.

   7. jungle
      desert
      house
      park

ANSWERS

1 Who is Who?
1. Barbara
2. do
3. for
4. both
5. by
6. glasses

2 The Perfect Room
1. our
2. for
3. Fred
4. living
5. room
6. drew

3
1. sports
2. stereo
3. at
4. have
5. place
6. build

4 Kitty Adopts Sonya
1. fish
2. like
3. sing
4. birthday
5. bird
6. shop

5
1. become
2. pet
3. know
4. walking
5. cat
6. adopted

6 Mother's Hand
1. hand
2. in
3. help
4. until
5. mother
6. knew

7
1. asked
2. mixed
3. by
4. Mom
5. fruit
6. help

8 The Block Party
1. houses
2. but
3. school
4. Look
5. to
6. friends

9
1. lots
2. at
3. make
4. for
5. made
6. party

10 The Barking Fish
1. body
2. took
3. fish
4. onto
5. dog
6. after

11
1. went
2. lion
3. take
4. fish
5. to
6. into

12 Next Door
1. for
2. truck
3. carried
4. children
5. tables
6. of

13
1. with
2. Amy
3. house
4. were
5. later
6. teachers

14 April Fool
1. on
2. first
3. these
4. months
5. year
6. twelve

15
1. moved
2. changed
3. parties
4. people
5. when
6. April

16 His Father's Mouse
1. loudly
2. with
3. mouse
4. work
5. lawyer
6. for

17
1. were
2. mouse
3. his
4. computers
5. like
6. desk

18 Lunch Money
1. up
2. bus
3. wrong
4. bring
5. into
6. money

19
1. was
2. stopped
3. stores
4. walked
5. There
6. happy

20 A Happy Birthday
1. party
2. little
3. games
4. birthday
5. age
6. than

21
1. for
2. did
3. present
4. name
5. just
6. under

22 Kenny Joins a Team
1. every
2. team
3. lonely
4. sport
5. basketball
6. near

23
1. hit
2. join
3. But
4. team
5. most
6. being

24 Gregory's Garden
1. farm
2. play
3. shy
4. fence
5. to
6. garden

25
1. in
2. told
3. children
4. grow
5. have
6. friends

26 The Chinese Bowl
1. what
2. loved
3. over
4. bowl
5. table
6. hit

27
1. purpose
2. her
3. about
4. pieces
5. antiques
6. store

28 The Museum Lollipop
1. sticky
2. lollipops
3. museum
4. at
5. him
6. though

29
1. at
2. lollipop
3. was
4. leader
5. statue
6. happily

30 Kate and Jimmy
1. foot
2. stuck
3. on
4. must
5. gum
6. do

31
1. but
2. clean
3. window
4. left
5. quiet
6. to
7. Jimmy

32 Parrots as Pets
1. cages
2. their
3. more
4. people
5. parrot
6. cage
7. words

33
1. years
2. holes
3. trouble
4. warm
5. When

ANSWERS

6. parrot
7. polite

34 Money in the Bank
1. When
2. going
3. saved
4. before
5. money
6. bank
7. have

35
1. closed
2. of
3. sign
4. slip
5. more
6. told
7. bank

36 The Bulldog
1. always
2. strong
3. mean
4. bulldogs
5. at
6. scared
7. ugly

37
1. take
2. wider
3. puppy
4. won't
5. at
6. hold
7. dog

38 The Open Door
1. called
2. to
3. secret
4. closet
5. keeps
6. long
7. closet

39
1. open
2. dusted
3. print
4. quiet
5. with
6. closet
7. door

40 The Secret Club
1. members
2. club
3. name
4. because
5. think
6. have
7. allowed

41
1. invite
2. start
3. fun
4. all
5. secret
6. friends'
7. club

42 The City Fair
1. who
2. clapped
3. never
4. pig
5. farmer
6. longer
7. pig

43
1. farmer
2. on
3. like
4. laugh
5. terrible
6. cloak
7. sounds

44 Nail Soup
1. strange
2. food
3. at
4. figure
5. had
6. water
7. food

45
1. Who
2. taste
3. salt
4. would
5. once
6. soup
7. bone

46 An American King
1. king
2. tribes
3. by
4. different
5. settlers
6. chief
7. union

47
1. in
2. Indians
3. destroyed
4. killed
5. helped
6. fought
7. part

48 The Talking Picture
1. used
2. After

3. mine
4. voice
5. scared
6. no
7. piano

49
1. next
2. entire
3. talking
4. woman
5. oldest
6. picture
7. smile

50 Special Class
1. her
2. liked
3. funny
4. could
5. friend
6. from
7. Laura

51
1. why
2. teacher
3. change
4. called
5. leave
6. going
7. Special

52 A Birthday Card
1. use
2. paper
3. plain
4. needed
5. card
6. officer's
7. with

53
1. I'll
2. mother
3. kitchen
4. handwriting
5. around
6. Then
7. recipe

54
1. finding
2. under
3. gone
4. ruined
5. kitchen
6. were
7. card

55 The Inventor
1. deaf
2. greatest
3. about
4. hatch
5. questions

6. job
7. train

56
1. station
2. instead
3. next
4. book
5. changed
6. player
7. thought

57
1. movies
2. other
3. shout
4. typists
5. inventions
6. common
7. without

58 A Pet for Patricia
1. rid
2. kitten
3. going
4. if
5. parents
6. care
7. keeper

59
1. sleeping
2. yard
3. growl
4. carry
5. over
6. lion
7. Kitty

60
1. when
2. ate
3. sleepy
4. bed
5. just
6. home
7. kitten

61
1. pieces
2. lion
3. captured
4. break
5. sleeps
6. hair
7. pet

62 I'm Not Your Friend
1. party
2. correct
3. dozen
4. for
5. mother
6. isn't
7. friend

63
1. back

2. Meggin's
3. later
4. shelves
5. walked
6. waiting
7. special

64
1. because
2. feelings
3. school
4. nasty
5. waiting
6. bet
7. friend

65
1. said
2. feelings
3. loyal
4. even
5. your
6. friend
7. party

66 Up, Up, and Away
1. lessons
2. before
3. raised
4. classroom
5. blow
6. instead

67
1. work
2. airships
3. blimp
4. over
5. balloon
6. experiment
7. bring

68
1. balloon
2. letter
3. outside
4. floating
5. circled
6. forever
7. passed

69
1. classroom
2. famous
3. speak
4. disappointed
5. in
6. Paul
7. balloon

70 The Dunking Booth
1. class
2. brought
3. band
4. But
5. Trent
6. booth

7. carnival

71
1. than
2. pick
3. that
4. Jeffrey
5. fortune
6. boring
7. pointed

72
1. hit
2. dunked
3. excited
4. idea
5. mean
6. to
7. class

73
1. Garcia's
2. better
3. Assistant
4. booth
5. When
6. carnival
7. dunked

74 The Silver Trumpet
1. as
2. Violins
3. hear
4. instrument
5. trumpet
6. loud
7. neighbors

75
1. racket
2. singing
3. when
4. loud
5. alone
6. Nancy
7. trumpet

76
1. schools
2. upstairs
3. hard
4. speech
5. until
6. stage
7. seated

77
1. played
2. high
3. smiled
4. to
5. trumpet
6. proud
7. loud

78 Vincent's Vacation
1. relax
2. perfect

3. vacation
4. father
5. few
6. holiday
7. guessed

79
1. really
2. best
3. washing
4. for
5. sleeping
6. Vincent
7. vacation
8. work

80
1. addresses
2. climbed
3. taking
4. first
5. broken
6. father
7. stuck
8. truck

81
1. tools
2. helper
3. had
4. hands
5. strong
6. hold
7. without
8. working

82 Three O'Clock
1. street
2. eating
3. waiter
4. at
5. locked
6. through
7. set
8. night

83
1. trucks
2. coming
3. fish
4. sound
5. airplaine
6. wonder
7. at
8. booths

84
1. medicine
2. smile
3. clean
4. closes
5. country
6. because
7. fix
8. leak

85
1. telephone

2. answer
3. people
4. walk
5. open
6. dawn
7. day
8. bed

86 The Indian Child
1. special
2. scarce
3. from
4. name
5. picked
6. food
7. father
8. hunter

87
1. better
2. at
3. much
4. shy
5. knife
6. bear
7. name
8. hunters

88
1. when
2. helping
3. hunters
4. help
5. himself
6. never
7. enough
8. grow

89
1. part
2. ground
3. plants
4. great
5. food
6. than
7. name
8. farmers

90 Teddy's Loose Tooth
1. problem
2. trouble
3. not
4. at
5. lick
6. front
7. watch
8. tooth

91
1. are
2. doing
3. whole
4. for
5. stage
6. recite
7. assembly

ANSWERS

8. tooth

92
1. about
2. chair
3. fine
4. sense
5. begged
6. go
7. leave
8. tooth

93
1. door
2. mouth
3. yanked
4. clothes
5. school
6. On
7. tooth
8. last

94 Planet of Balloons
1. planet
2. old
3. suit
4. huge
5. at
6. nearing
7. moon
8. astronauts

95
1. landing
2. coming
3. up
4. height
5. planet
6. balloon
7. moon
8. guest

96
1. friendly
2. started
3. needles
4. pop
5. find
6. in
7. people
8. dived

97
1. rock
2. birds
3. home
4. gathered
5. air
6. shouted
7. Next
8. slingshot

98 The Kite Parade
1. string
2. name
3. kite
4. try

5. back
6. haul
7. headed
8. toy

99
1. along
2. toward
3. barking
4. boat
5. catch
6. kite
7. pond
8. behind

100
1. with
2. skates
3. foot
4. calling
5. heard
6. wind
7. right
8. rope

101
1. too
2. because
3. boat
4. cooked
5. died
6. chasing
7. kite
8. free

102 The Lamp of Truth
1. rooms
2. chairs
3. children's
4. furniture
5. lady
6. If
7. difficult
8. chairs

103
1. mystery
2. chests
3. with
4. attic
5. dresses
6. eyes
7. full
8. door

104
1. found
2. read
3. shine
4. permission
5. downstairs
6. with
7. light
8. lantern

105
1. about
2. powers

3. lamp
4. shining
5. truth
6. lantern
7. game
8. light

106 The Crime of Bowling
1. themselves
2. wooden
3. bowling
4. over
5. game
6. smaller
7. sports
8. law

107
1. playing
2. at
3. equipment
4. town
5. stones
6. forest
7. ninepins
8. pins

108
1. Connecticut
2. breaking
3. of
4. honest
5. law
6. pins
7. Bowling
8. ninepins

109 Exercises: Phonograms
1. buzzing
2. book
3. spoiled
4. flute
5. whale
6. thought
7. page
8. farm
9. pail
10. allow
11. yellow

110 Exercises: Main Idea
1. kite
2. science
3. named
4. bowling
5. April
6. lollipop

111 Exercises: Details
1. green
2. change
3. table
4. shopping

5. front
6. sailors

112 Exercises: Structure
1. very
2. quickly
3. safe
4. faster
5. were
6. allowed
7. then
8. belongs
9. is
10. excellent
11. strong

113 Exercises: Relationships
1. of
2. over
3. before
4. for
5. from
6. behind
7. because
8. of
9. after
10. between
11. into

114 Exercises: Inference
1. strong
2. fire
3. presents
4. garden
5. boiling
6. write
7. money
8. solved
9. pet
10. below
11. scared

115 Exercises: Vocabulary Development
1. remove
2. rise
3. cats
4. looks
5. eat
6. together
7. trick
8. copy

116 Exercises: Broad Context
1. town
2. classroom
3. home
4. museum
5. birthday
6. car
7. park